530

i.WK

**This book is to be returned on or before
the last date stamped below.**

The Supported Learning in Physics Project
has received major support from

ESSEX

PHYSICS ON THE MOVE

This unit was written by
Chris Butlin with Maureen Maybank

The project is also supported by
The Department for Education and
Employment

THE SUPPORTED LEARNING IN PHYSICS PROJECT

Management Group

Elizabeth Whitelegg, Project Director, The Open University

Professor Dick West, National Power Professor of Science Education, The Open University

Christopher Edwards, Project Coordinator

Professor Mike Westbrook, Vice-President for Education, Industry and Public Affairs, The Institute of Physics

George Davies, Manager, College Recruitment, Ford of Britain

Geoff Abraham, Project Trailing Manager

Dorrie Giles, Schools Liaison Manager, Institution of Electrical Engineers

Martin Tims, Manager, Education Programme, Esso UK

Catherine Wilson, Education Manager (Schools and Colleges), Institute of Physics

Production

This unit was written for the Project by Chris Butlin, Institute of Physics, with Maureen Maybank.

Other members of the production team for this unit were:

Elizabeth Whitelegg, Project Director

Christopher Edwards, Project Coordinator

Andrew Coleman, Editor

John Coleman, Course Assessor

Alison George, Illustrator

Maureen Maybank, Unit Assessor

Julie Lynch, Project Secretary

Sian Lewis, Designer

The authors and Director wish to thank David Tawney and Mike Burton for their helpful comments and advice whilst writing this unit.

ISBN 0 435 68846 4

The Institute of Physics, 76 Portland Place, London, W1N 4AA.

First published 1996 by Heinemann Educational Publishers.

© 1996 The Institute of Physics.

Printed in Great Britain by Bath Press Colourbooks, Glasgow

For further information on the Supported Learning in Physics Project contact the Information and Marketing Officer, The Centre for Science Education, The Open University, Walton Hall, Milton Keynes, MK7 6AA.

1.1

CONTENTS

The SLIPP units introduce you to a new method of studying – one that you probably won't have used before. They will provide you with a way of studying on your own, or sometimes in small groups with other students in your class. Your teacher will be available to guide you in your use of this unit – giving you advice and help when they are needed and monitoring your progress – but mainly you will learn about this topic through your own study of this unit and the practical work associated with it.

We expect that you will study the unit during your normal physics lessons and also at other times – during free periods and homework sessions. Your teacher will give you guidance on how much time you need to spend on it. Your study will involve you in a variety of activities – you won't find yourself just reading the text, you will have to do some practical work (which we have called 'Explorations') and answer questions in the text as you go along. (Advice on how long each exploration is likely to take is given.) It is very important that you do answer the questions as you go along, rather than leaving them until you reach the end of a section (or indeed the end of the unit!), as they are there to help you to check whether you have understood the preceding text. If you find that you can't answer a question, then you should go over the relevant bit of text again. Some questions are followed immediately by their answers but you should resist the temptation to read the answer before you have thought about the question. If you find this difficult it may be a good idea to cover up the answer with a piece of paper while you think about the question. Other slightly longer or more demanding questions have their answers at the back of the section. Most sections also have a few difficult questions at the end. You are likely to need help with these; this might be from a teacher or from working with other students.

Most sections start with a short 'Ready to Study' test. You should do this before reading any further to check that you have all the necessary knowledge to start the section. The answers for this test are also at the end of the section. If you have any difficulties with these questions, you should look back through your old GCSE notes to see if they can help you or discuss your difficulties with your teacher, who may decide to go over certain areas with you before you start the section or recommend a textbook that will help you.

The large number of practical explorations in the unit are designed to let you thoroughly immerse yourself in the topic and involve yourself in some real science. It is only after hands-on experiences that you really begin to think about and understand a situation. We suggest that you do some of these explorations with other students who are studying the unit and, when appropriate, present your results to the rest of the class. Because there are such a large number of these explorations it would be impossible for you to do all of them, so if everyone shares their results with others in the class you will all find out about some of the explorations that you are unable to do.

HOW TO USE THIS UNIT

Your teacher will arrange times when the practical work can be undertaken. For health and safety reasons you must be properly supervised during laboratory sessions and your teacher will be responsible for running these sessions in accordance with your school's or college's normal health and safety procedures.

HEALTH AND SAFETY NOTE

The unit warns you about any potential hazards and suggests precautions whenever risk assessments are required of an employer under the Management of Health and Safety at Work Regulations 1992. We expect that employers will accept these precautions as forming the basis for risk assessments and as equivalent to those they normally advocate for school science. If teachers or technicians have any doubts, they should consult their employers.

However, in providing these warnings and suggestions, we make the assumption that practical work is conducted in a properly equipped and maintained laboratory and that field work takes account of any LEA or school or college guidelines on safe conduct. We also assume that care is taken with normal laboratory operations, such as heating and handling heavy objects, and that good laboratory practice is observed at all times.

Any mains-operated equipment should be properly maintained and the output from signal generators, amplifiers, etc., should not exceed 25 V rms.

We take transportation very much for granted these days. Yet only two hundred years ago even short journeys were quite a trial and many people never ventured further than the next town. There were no cars, no bicycles, no trains and no aeroplanes. The only options were to travel by horse, by boat or on foot, and owing to the cost of horses, most people travelled on foot. Make some rough estimates of the distance that you can travel in a day on foot, on horseback, driving and flying, and compare them with each other. Changes in travel opportunities have had a great effect on society.

Although the means of transport have undergone enormous change, the purposes of transportation systems have remained essentially the same: namely, the safe and efficient movement of people and goods from place to place, without injury to people or damage to goods.

In this unit we will look at the physics involved in moving people and products about. Although you will have studied all of the ideas to a certain level in your earlier science courses, the many sections in this unit will enable you to revise and extend your knowledge and understanding of forces, dynamics, statics, energy, motion, electricity and electromagnetism.

Most of the activities in this unit are about vehicles

toppling over

decelerating too quickly in accidents

colliding

braking

exploding.

A fun-packed collection! Of course, the physics is concerned with making all these as non-life-threatening as possible. You will also be involved with analysing information in order to make recommendations.

INTRODUCTION

7

2

You will be well aware of the fact that some vehicles are a lot more stable than others. It is rare to see a racing car turn over and yet one often hears about tall lorries and caravans tipping on to their sides. Off-road four-wheel drive vehicles have now become very popular for use on roads, but they have been developed to cope with rough and steep terrain even with loose or muddy surfaces. As a result their design makes them less stable on roads than normal cars. We will be considering the factors affecting a vehicle's stability in this section.

If you have access to the video *QED – Testing, testing* (BBC Manchester, 1984) it would be helpful to watch it before studying this section. This video shows tractors being toppled over to test the performance of their protective cabs.

READY TO STUDY TEST

Before you begin this section you should be able to:

■ draw and interpret force diagrams, including representing the weight of a body as a vertical force that acts from a single point, known as the centre of gravity

■ describe weight as the force of gravity on mass and quote g, the force per unit mass ($g = 9.81 \text{ N kg}^{-1}$), to an appropriate number of significant figures in calculations (you may well be more used to $g = 9.81 \text{ m s}^{-2}$ and to thinking of it in terms of an acceleration of an object in free-fall)

■ locate the centre of gravity for objects that have simple symmetrical shapes

- define equilibrium
- calculate unknown forces for simple cases of equilibrium with parallel forces
- balance a see-saw by adjusting the position or size of people on it, using:

$$F_{\text{left}} \times x_{\text{left}} = F_{\text{right}} \times x_{\text{right}}$$

Where F is the weight of a person and x is their distance from the pivot of the see-saw.

QUESTIONS

R1 Where is the centre of gravity of each of the following shapes?

(a) A metre ruler.   (c) A hollow ring.

(b) A circular disc. (d) A triangle.

R2 If an object is in a state of equilibrium, we say that it is in a state of no overall change.

(a) What sorts of change indicate that something is *not* in a state of equilibrium?

(b) If an object is in a state of equilibrium, what would you expect to be true about the forces acting on it?

R3 (a) You are on a see-saw and find that your end is going down. How can you use other people or adjust your position so that your end of the see-saw goes up?

(b) A person of 45 N weight, sitting 1.0 m from the centre of a see-saw, balances another person sitting 1.5 m away on the other side. How much does the second person weigh?

R4 If the metre ruler in Figure 2.1 is not moving, what can you say about the sizes of R, W, F_1 and F_2?

Figure 2.1

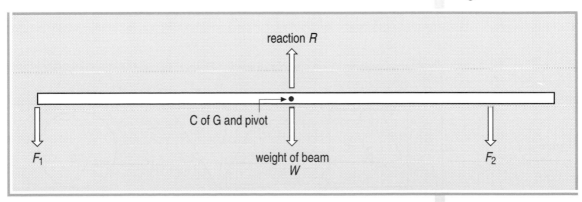

2.1 Stability

A key factor determining whether a vehicle will be stable is the position of its **centre of gravity** – the point through which its entire **weight** can be considered to act. This is not quite the same as the **centre of mass**, which is the point that acts as if all the **mass** were concentrated there, although the two points usually do coincide. (They only fail to coincide when the object is in a **non-uniform gravitational field**.)

So let us look at what causes a vehicle to be stable or unstable. It is common practice to talk about stability in terms of the **equilibrium** or state of balance of an object. Three states are possible: stable, unstable and neutral. These are identified by the direction of displacement of the object's centre of gravity when a force is applied to it and then removed.

 What can you say about the centre of gravity's position when an object is as stable as possible?

The centre of gravity is as low as possible.

 Using Table 2.1, identify the equilibrium states of the objects in Figure 2.2.

The square is in stable equilibrium; the triangle is in unstable equilibrium; the circle is in neutral equilibrium.

Table 2.1 States of equilibrium

Equilibrium state	Displacement of centre of gravity when force is applied	Displacement of centre of gravity when force is removed
Neutral	Stays at the same level	Stays at the same level
Stable	Rises	Returns to original level
Unstable	Falls	Continues to fall

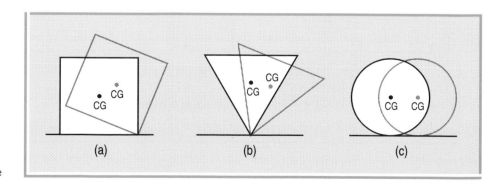

Figure 2.2
(a) Displaced square,
(b) displaced triangle,
(c) displaced circle

An object is pivoted so that it can hang freely in space in as stable a position as possible (imagine a nail through a corner of the triangle). When it settles, where will its centre of gravity be?

The centre of gravity will be vertically below the point of suspension. It will then rise if a force moves it to one side or the other; returning the object to its former position when that force is removed.

2.2 Moments

Whether or not objects remain stable or tip over has to do with the **principle of moments**, something you have probably used without realizing it when dealing with balance beams. You may like to remind yourself of the ideas by trying the following question.

Q1 Many railway stations have coin in the slot ticket machines. The simplest designs make use of a balance beam to test whether the coin inserted is of the right type.

After a coin has been placed in the slot it drops on to an oddly shaped balance beam as shown in Figure 2.3.

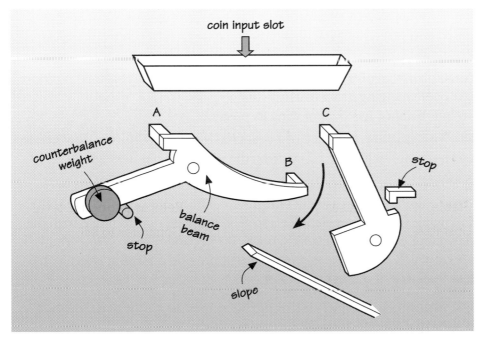

Figure 2.3
Coin balance beam system

If the coin is too large it gets caught on latches A and C and goes no further until it is rejected. If it is too small it just drops through between latches A and B and is rejected. If it is about the right diameter it rests on latches A and B, but without getting caught on C. At this stage a test of the coin's weight can be made. If it is heavy enough, the balance beam will turn in the direction of the large arrow and tip the coin on to the slope

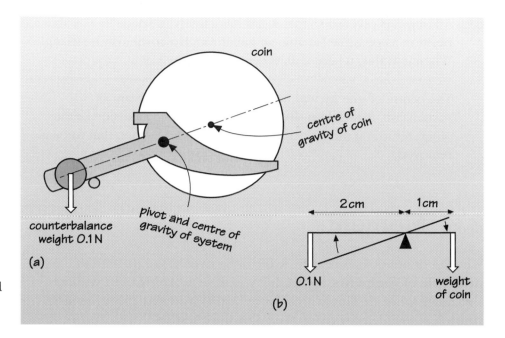

Figure 2.4
(a) A real beam and
(b) a simple
representation of it

and so accept it. Think of this system as a simple balance beam as shown in Figure 2.4.

(a) Which of the following weight coins will tip on to the slope: 0.05 N, 0.1 N, 0.15 N, 0.25 N? (*Hint:* Think about which coins will give a greater turning effect than the counterbalance weight.)

(b) If you wished to allow through a coin of less weight, what change could you make to (i) the counterbalance weight, (ii) the counterbalance position?

(c) Explain the advantage(s) that (i) moving the counterbalance position has over changing its weight, (ii) changing the weight of the counterbalance has over moving its position.

(d) With inflation, the price of a ticket has gone up. The coin now needed has its centre of gravity 1.2 cm from the pivot and has a weight of 0.2 N.

If the counterbalance weight remains 2 cm from the pivot, which of the following is the *best* weight for it to be if the system is to rotate with the new coin? Choose from 0.05 N, 0.1 N, 0.15 N and 0.25 N. (*Hint:* Think about which counterbalance weight will provide a turning effect a little less than that of the new coin.) ◆

Q2 Suggest other methods that might be used to check that the coins placed in a slot machine are the correct ones. ◆

In obtaining the answers to Question 1 you will have simply multiplied the weight of the coin by the distance between its centre of gravity and the pivot, and compared this value with the product of the weight of the counterbalance and the distance between its centre of gravity and the pivot. Whichever was the larger determined the way the beam would rotate or tip. What you were doing was calculating the **moments** of the forces about a chosen axis (in this case the pivot). Simply, this is found by multiplying a force by a distance. In general, you will have to be more precise about the distance part of that formula to cover all eventualities. The full definition is as follows. The moment T of a force is given by

$$T = F \times x$$

where F is the value of the force acting and x is the perpendicular distance from the chosen axis to the line of action of the force. You should learn this. It is illustrated in Figure 2.5.

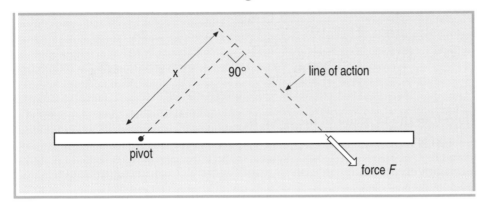

Figure 2.5
Force F and line of action

Look at the following example.

Example (a)

A nut is just loosened by a force of 100 N applied 0.15 m from its centre in the direction shown in Figure 2.6.

 What is the moment of this force about the centre of the nut?

The moment is simply the force applied multiplied by the perpendicular distance of its line of action from the centre of the nut. Hence 100 N × 0.15m = 15 N m. (*Note:* Whilst the calculation of a moment does involve the product of a force and a distance, the distance is *not* the distance moved along the line of action of the force – that is *work done*, which has units of joules. To distinguish between them N m is used for moments.)

It is slightly more tricky if the force is applied at an angle, as in the situation in Figure 2.7.

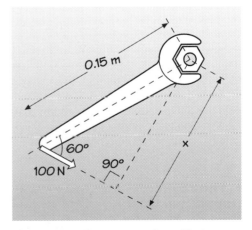

Figure 2.6 Spanner and perpendicular applied force

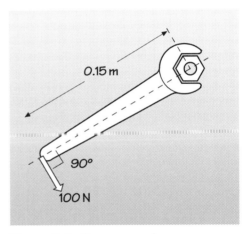

Figure 2.7 Spanner and applied force at an angle

13

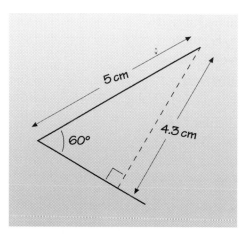

Figure 2.8
Scale diagram

Example (b)

Again find the moment of the force about the centre of the nut.

You could find x by drawing a scale diagram like Figure 2.8. Here we have drawn 5.0 cm to represent 0.15 m. The angle remains at 60°, so we find by measuring that the length representing x is 4.3 cm. So

$$x = 4.3\,\text{cm} \times \frac{0.15\,\text{m}}{5.0\,\text{cm}}$$

$$= 0.129\,\text{m}$$

$$= 0.13\,\text{m (to two significant figures)}$$

Therefore the moment of the force is

$$100\,\text{N} \times 0.13\,\text{m} = 13\,\text{N m}$$

Alternatively, we can calculate x from Figure 2.7 using trigonometry:

$$\sin 60° = \frac{\text{opposite side}}{\text{hypotenuse}}$$

$$= \frac{x}{0.15\,\text{m}}$$

So

$$x = 0.15\,\text{m} \times \sin 60°$$

$$= 0.15\,\text{m} \times 0.8660$$

$$= 0.1299\,\text{m}$$

$$= 0.13\,\text{m (to two significant figures)}$$

Therefore the moment of the force is

$$100\,\text{m} \times 0.13\,\text{m} = 13\,\text{N m}$$

Q3 What is the moment of the force if it is applied as shown in Figure 2.9? ◆

Q4 To tighten various nuts holding engine parts together by the correct amount, a special spanner called a **torque** wrench is used.

Calculate the force that has to be applied at the end of the torque wrench if the perpendicular distance between the line of action of this force and the centre of the nut is 0.42 m and the moment of the force is 170 N m. ◆

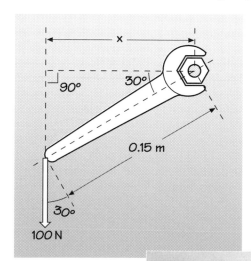

Figure 2.9
Spanner with 100 N force at a different angle

A torque wrench

14

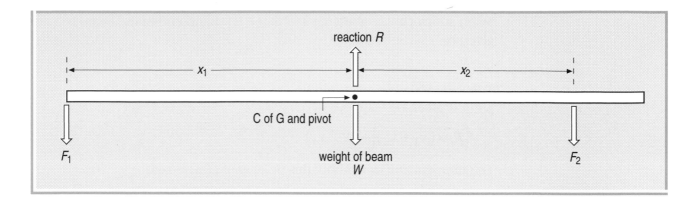

Exploring moments

Figure 2.10
Balance beam and
forces F_1 and F_2

If we now return to a simple see-saw situation with a number of parallel forces acting we can explore the principle of moments more fully.

The moment about the centre of gravity of the beam tending to rotate it in an anticlockwise direction is given by

$$F_1 \times x_1$$

and the moment about the centre of gravity of the beam tending to rotate it in a clockwise direction is given by

$$F_2 \times x_2$$

The moment due to the weight of the beam about its centre of gravity is given by

$$W \times 0$$

The moment due to the reaction R from the pivot about the centre of gravity is given by

$$R \times 0$$

For the system to be in a state of equilibrium, the sum of the clockwise moments about any point must be equal to the sum of the anticlockwise moments about that same point. So in this situation, where the chosen point was the pivot at which the centre of gravity of the beam was situated, we have

$$F_1 \times x_1 = F_2 \times x_2$$

You should learn this.

Taking moments about the centre of gravity of the beam means that neither the weight W of the beam nor the reaction R from the pivot play any part – as their distances from the pivot are zero their moments are also zero.

If the size of F_1 is reduced and the centre of gravity is at the centre of the beam, then the beam would not balance, or be in equilibrium, unless x_1 is sufficiently increased or x_2 sufficiently reduced.

It can get a little more complex if moments are taken about other points, but the result is the same. For example, the moment tending to rotate the beam anticlockwise about an axis at the left-hand end of the beam is given by

$$R \times x_1$$

The sum of the moments tending to rotate the beam clockwise about this point is given by

$$\left[F_2 \times (x_1 + x_2)\right] + (W \times x_1)$$

The moment due to F_1 about this point is of course zero.

So for equilibrium we must have

$$R \times x_1 = \left[F_2 \times (x_1 + x_2)\right] + (W \times x_1)$$

However, as you might have guessed, the reaction at the pivot R must be given by

$$R = F_1 + F_2 + W$$

in magnitude, though opposite in direction, so

$$\left[(F_1 + F_2 + W) \times x_1\right] = \left[F_2 \times (x_1 + x_2)\right] + (W \times x_1)$$

If you expand this equation carefully you should end up with

$$F_1 \times x_1 = F_2 \times x_2$$

which is the same condition that you had before, even though moments were taken about a different point. (*Hint:* To save time in calculations it often helps to take moments about a point where some values will be zero.)

Now think about how these calculations can be useful in real life: what might make a fork-lift truck tip over? (See Figure 2.11.)

To make it easier at this stage, let us consider the forces acting in the vertical plane only. W is the weight of the fork-lift truck acting at its centre of gravity. R_1 and R_2 are the vertical components of the forces with which the slope is pushing up on the wheels.

Taking moments about an axis through the lowest point of contact of the tyre on the lower wheel and the slope we have:

moment tending to rotate the truck clockwise = $W \times x_1$

moment tending to rotate the truck anticlockwise = $R_2 \times (x_1 + x_2)$

 Why is there no moment due to R_1?

R_1 acts at the point about which moments are being taken, therefore the distance from its line of action to that point is zero and so its moment is also zero.

should give you an idea of how to find its centre of gravity in the plane So

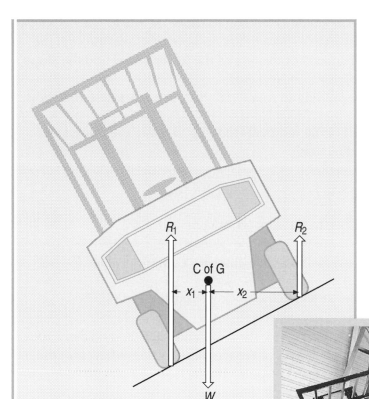

Figure 2.11 Forces on a tilting fork-lift truck (the lengths of the arrows are not necessarily representative of the sizes of the forces)

So, for equilibrium

$$W \times x_1 = R_2 \times (x_1 + x_2)$$

Now consider the situation shown in Figure 2.12.

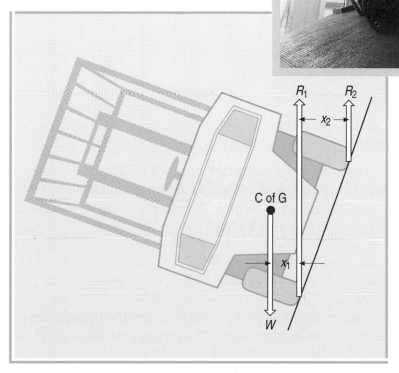

Figure 2.12 Fork-lift truck tilted further

17

What is/are the moment(s) tending to rotate the truck in a clockwise direction? It may help to take moments about the axis through the lowest point of contact of the tyre of the lower wheel and the slope.

There are none tending to rotate the truck in a clockwise direction.

 What is the sum of the moments tending to rotate the truck in an anticlockwise direction?

$$(W \times x_1) + (R_2 \times x_2)$$

 What must happen to the fork-lift truck?

It must topple over in an anticlockwise direction.

 What is the point at which the truck just begins to topple?

When the centre of gravity of the fork-lift truck is immediately above the lowest point of contact of the tyre of the lower wheel and the slope. This is, of course, the point at which any clockwise moment, which would restore stability, disappears.

 What is the advantage of having a low centre of gravity?

The angle at which it will topple will be larger if the centre of gravity is lower, as shown in the Figure 2.13.

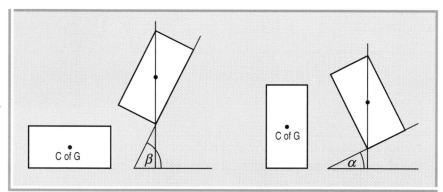

Figure 2.13
Diagram showing that angle β is greater than α

 When the centre of gravity of the fork-lift truck is just to the left of the lowest point of contact of the tyre of the lower wheel and the slope, the truck continues to topple. To what point will the centre of gravity move before it stops toppling?

To the lowest point it can get to.

If you were able to watch the video (*QED – Testing, testing*) that we mentioned at the beginning of the unit, you will realize the importance of knowing the centre of gravity of a tractor. The photograph on page 17 of one of Boss Group Limited's fork-lift trucks undergoing a 'topple test' should give you an idea of how to find its centre of gravity in the plane shown. However, it is also possible to find its centre of gravity in the other plane (from front to back) too. In addition, you can investigate how the position of the centre of gravity is affected by (a) the load carried, and (b) the height of the load on the forks.

The following exploration describes how to do these investigations.

 Exploration 2.1   Investigating centres of gravity

Apparatus:

◆ model tractor (e.g. Britains' Ford Model 8730 1/32nd scale – carefully remove the coupling from the rear of this model)   ◆ model fork-lift truck (e.g. Britains' Sanderson's Rough Terrain Fork-lift Truck 1/32nd scale)   ◆ top-pan balance   ◆ ruler   ◆ protractor   ◆ lead shot   ◆ Blu-Tack   ◆ thread   ◆ ramp

Thinking about things first

Tractors and fork-lift trucks are three-dimensional objects, each with its centre of gravity somewhere 'inside' it. Each is symmetrical in one plane (left to right as you look at its front). You can use that symmetry to find the height of the centre of gravity above the base but not how close it is to the rear wheels. For that you will need a different technique.

They both have to be stable in use in *all* directions, but can you see that loading them at the front will make them more likely to topple forwards?

Make notes only of those details of the physics that you think will be of general application in your future revision, i.e. the general practical methods and ways of processing the data.

Part (i) To find the centre of gravity about the model's symmetrical axis by tilting

Position the tractor or fork-lift truck on the ramp. Fix small pieces of Blu-Tack on to the ramp alongside the tyres that are lower down the slope to stop the model sliding down the slope, as shown in Fiigure 2.14 overleaf. Do not fix the Blu-Tack to the tyres. Also fix the movable wheels so that they are pointing forwards. Devise a method of catching the model safely when it topples.

Slowly tip the ramp until the model just topples, noting the angle of the ramp as this occurs.

Cut out pieces of cardboard the exact size and shape as an outline of the back view of the tractor and the fork end of the fork-lift truck. Assuming that the vehicles are symmetrical about the vertical axis, draw a line vertically through the middle of each piece of card. The centres of gravity must lie along these lines. The outlines shown in Figure 2.15 overleaf match the specified model tractor and fork-lift truck.

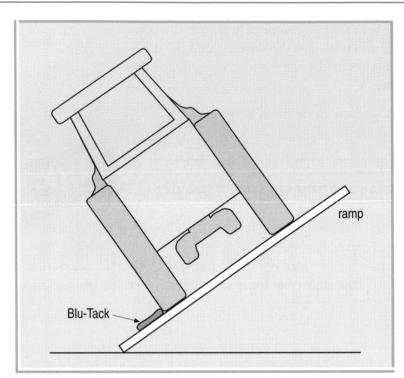

Figure 2.14
Arrangement of the model on the ramp

ramp

Blu-Tack

Figure 2.15
Outlines of card shapes

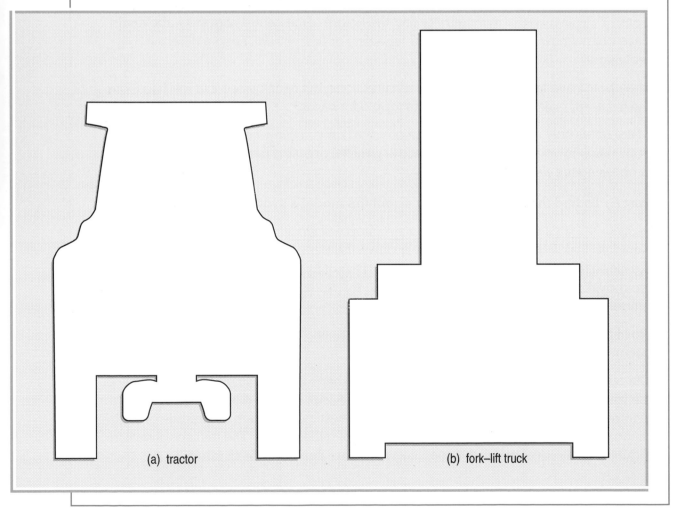

(a) tractor

(b) fork–lift truck

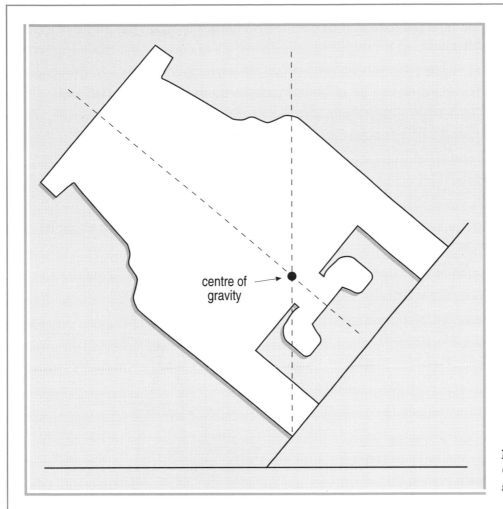

Figure 2.16
Cardboard
shape on slope

Draw, on a piece of paper, a representation of the slope to show the angle at which the model just toppled. Place the cardboard shape on the slope you have just drawn. From the bottom corner of the cardboard shape draw a line vertically upwards as shown in Figure 2.16. The model's centre of gravity must lie along this line too. Where the two lines on the cardboard shape meet is the model's centre of gravity in that plane. (Your report should include an explanation of why this is so.)

(*Note:* For a real tractor or fork-lift truck this same process would apply. You would, however, need to construct everything – mass and dimensions – to scale in order to find its centre of gravity.)

Part (ii) Investigate how the load and its position on the forks affect the angle of topple of a model fork-lift truck

First make a model 'straw bale' by embedding lead shot into Blu-Tack. Place this on the fork-lift truck's forks and measure the angle at which the model topples. Repeat the process several times using different amounts of lead shot and see how the angle at which the model topples varies.

Do be careful to control the variables. If you are investigating the effect of different loads then keep the position of the 'bale' on the forks fixed. If you are investigating the effect of different positions on the forks then keep the weight of the load fixed.

Part (iii) Locating the centre of gravity of a model tractor or fork-lift truck about its non-symmetrical axis

The following technique has been used commercially at the University of Cranfield's Agricultural Engineering Department to locate tractors' centres of gravity.

First, note the weight, W, of the model tractor by placing it on a top-pan balance. (*Note:* A mass of 1 kg weighs approximately 9.8 N.) Also measure the horizontal distance between the front and rear axles (L_1 in Figure 2.17).

Now place the tractor so that its rear wheels only are on the top-pan balance, while its front wheels are supported on a surface level with the top-pan, as in Figure 2.17. Note the weight, W_1, supported by the model's rear wheels.

Attach thread around both sides of the front axles of the model. Again with only the rear wheels on the top-pan, lift the front wheels vertically upwards 3 cm or so, as in Figure 2.18. Note the weight, W_2, supported by the rear wheels now. Note also the vertical distance, h, through which the front wheels have been lifted and the *horizontal* distance, L_2, now between the front and rear axles.

A tractor on a weighbridge

Using these measurements we can now calculate the centre of gravity of a model tractor in its non-symmetrical plane.

The force W_1 is shown as the reaction from the top-pan balance and it will be equal, but opposite in direction, to the weight applied by the rear wheels.

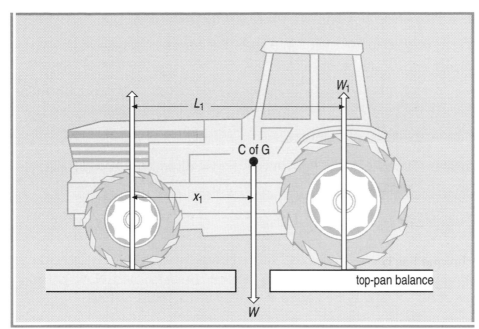

Figure 2.17
A model tractor with its rear wheels on a top-pan balance and its front wheels on a level surface (the lengths of the arrows are not necessarily representative of the sizes of the forces)

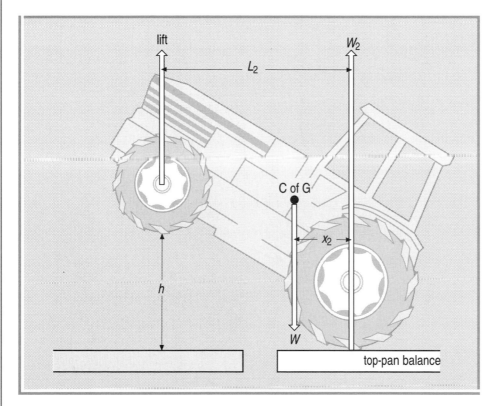

Figure 2.18
A model tractor with its rear wheels only on top-pan balance

Taking moments about the front axle we have:

moment tending to rotate the model in an anticlockwise direction = $W_1 \times L_1$

moment tending to rotate the model in a clockwise direction = $W \times x_1$

Since the system is in equilibrium we can write

$$W_1 \times L_1 = W \times x_1$$

Then, with W, W_1 and L_1 measured, the value of x_1 can be calculated.

However, knowing x_1 only enables us to draw a line – the centre of gravity will be *somewhere* along that line. To get the actual position another measurement is needed.

The tractor is lifted through a known angle as shown in Figure 2.18. (It is probably more convenient to measure the height the front wheels are raised rather than the angle.)

Taking moments about the front axle we have:

moment tending to rotate the model in an anticlockwise direction = $W \times (L_2 - x_2)$

moment tending to rotate the model in a clockwise direction = $W_2 \times l_2$

Since the system is again in equilibrium, we have

$$W \times (L_2 - x_2) = W_2 \times L_2$$

So, with W, W_2 and L_2 being measured, the value of x_2 can be calculated. Now that you know the positions of both x_1 and x_2 the centre of gravity in this plane can be determined.

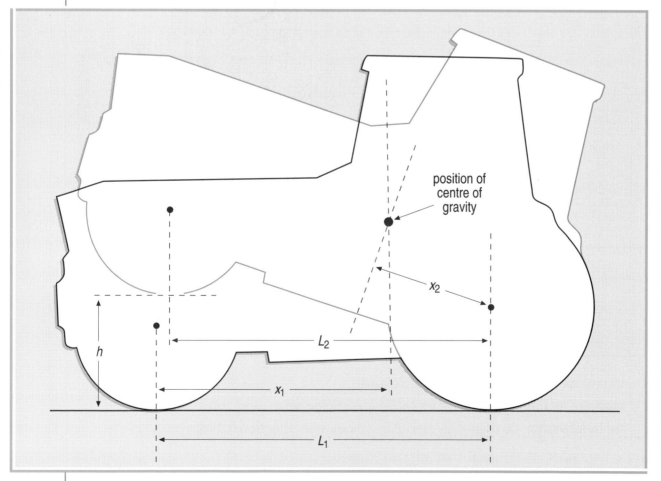

Figure 2.19 Cardboard shapes with lines marked

Make a cardboard cut-out of the side view of the model (as in Figure 2.19). Mark a vertical line on this cut-out a horizontal distance x_1 from the front axle position to show where the centre of gravity must lie. Rotate the cardboard cut-out until its front wheel has been lifted through a height h and then similarly mark another line a horizontal distance x_2 from the rear axle position. Where the two lines meet is where the model's centre of gravity in that plane lies.

(*Note:* For a real tractor this same process would apply. You would, however, need to construct everything – mass and dimensions – to scale in order to find its centre of gravity.)

Q5 A fork-lift truck has an unladen weight of 220 050 N and centre of gravity 1.914 m from the front axle. Loads placed on the forks are 2.10 m from the front axle (see Figure 2.20).

(a) What, in theory, is largest load that the truck could carry without toppling over?

(b) Why are the forks kept as close to the front axle as possible? ◆

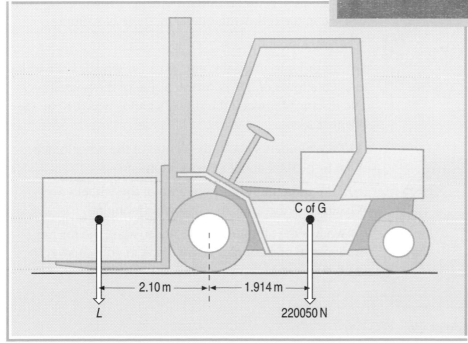

Figure 2.20

Q6 A car of weight 12 000 N has two front seat occupants whose combined weight is 1600 N. The wheelbase of the vehicle – the distance between the front and rear axles – is 3.50 m. The centre of gravity of the unladen vehicle is 2.00 m from the front axle and the centre of gravity of the occupants is 1.50 m from the front axle (see Figure 2.21).

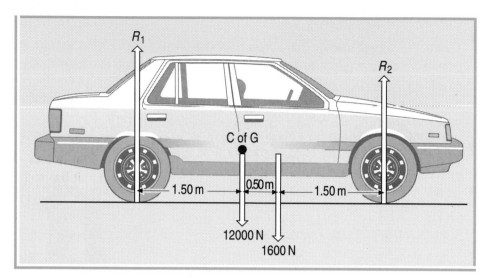

Figure 2.21
The forces acting on the car

Calculate the values of the reaction forces R_1 and R_2. What must the sum of these two reaction forces be equal to? ◆

Figure 2.22 Turning a tap

There are occasions when a pair of equal but opposite parallel forces are applied to provide a turning effect. A familiar example you can find at home is the turning of a tap (see Figure 2.22).

Calculating the torque, or moment, of a **couple**, is done in the same way as for all other moments. However, as you will see in the following question, there is a simple solution.

Q7 In order to undo the nuts on a car wheel, a driver had to exert a force of 200 N on each side of the wheelbrace. The distance between the driver's hands was 0.40 m. (See Figure 2.23.)

(a) Take moments about the centre of the wheelbrace. What is the total anticlockwise moment?

(b) Take moments about one end of the wheelbrace. What now is the total anticlockwise moment?

(c) What is the simplest way of calculating the torque, or moment, of a couple? (*Hint:* Look at your answer to (b).) ◆

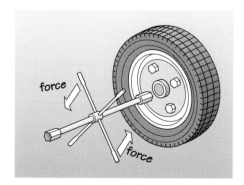

Figure 2.23 Using a wheelbrace

Achievements

After working through this section you should be able to:

- distinguish between stable, unstable and neutral equilibrium
- define and calculate the moment, or torque, of a force using

  $$T = F \times x \sin\theta$$

- describe the direction of a moment or torque as clockwise or anticlockwise
- apply the principle of moments to systems of parallel and non-parallel forces
- calculate the moment, or torque, of a couple
- locate a centre of gravity practically
- measure force and distance to a fair degree of accuracy.

Glossary

Centre of gravity   The point through which an object's entire weight can be considered to act. It coincides with the centre of mass unless the object is in a non-uniform gravitational field.

Centre of mass   The point that acts as if all of an object's mass were concentrated there. It usually coincides with the centre of gravity unless the object is in a non-uniform gravitational field.

Couple   A pair of parallel forces that produce a turning effect. They are equal in magnitude but opposite in direction.

Equilibrium   The state of balance of an object, be it stable, unstable or neutral. Each state is identified by the direction of displacement of an object's centre of gravity when a force is applied to it and then removed.

Gravitational field strength, g   The force on a unit mass ($N\,kg^{-1}$) as a result of it being in the gravitational field of another object, or the combined fields of several other objects. In a uniform gravitational field g is constant throughout the field, but in a *non*-uniform gravitational field g will vary from point to point. The further apart the field lines, the lower the value of g becomes. You may be more familiar with thinking of g as the acceleration due to gravity.

Mass   Unit: kilogram (kg). A measure of the inertia of an object – the degree of resistance it has to being accelerated or decelerated. An alternative definition, though perhaps rather less helpful, is that it is a measure of the amount of material in the object. An object's mass does not vary from place to place. Mass is a scalar quantity.

Moment   Unit: newton metre (N m). The moment of a force is a measure of its ability to rotate an object about a chosen axis. It is calculated by multiplying that force by its perpendicular distance from the chosen axis to the line of action of that force. Moment is a pseudo-vector quantity that is defined by a magnitude and the direction of an axis. An alternative name is torque.

Non-uniform gravitational field   A gravitational field where the field lines are not parallel. This results in a **gravitational field strength, g**, with a value that depends on position. In this situation the force per unit mass will vary depending on where the mass is. So for an object, when the force on each individual element of mass is added to the others, the point through which the resultant force acts might not be the centre of mass, but is the centre of gravity.

Principle of moments   If an object is in equilibrium then the algebraic sum of the moments acting on it about all axes is zero.

Torque   Unit: newton metre (N m). An alternative term for moment.

Weight   Unit: newton (N). The weight of an object is usually defined in one of two ways: (i) the force of gravitational attraction of a massive body (usually our Earth) for that object, or (ii) the downward force exerted by the object on its support. An object's weight will vary from place to place. Weight is a vector quantity.

Answers to Ready to Study test

R1

(a) At the centre of the ruler.

(b) At the centre of the disc.

(c) At the centre of the ring – even though there is nothing there!

(d) Along a line from one vertex to the centre of the opposite side. It is two-thirds of the way down this line from the vertex.

R2

(a) Any change in motion (i.e. acceleration, deceleration, rotation or change in direction of travel) indicates that an object is not in equilibrium.

(b) The forces acting on the object would be balanced forces – left and right forces would be balanced, up and down forces would be balanced, and so on.

R3

(a) You can put more people on the other end to use their added weight *or* you can move yourself towards the centre of the see-saw.

(b) The second person weighs 30 N.

R4

$$R = F_1 + F_2 + W$$

Answers to questions in the text

Q1

(a) 0.25 N only.

(b)(i) Reduce its weight; (ii) move it towards the pivot.

(c)(i) Cheap to change, no new part; (ii) easy to change, no skill or knowledge required.

(d) 0.1 N.

Q2

There are a vast number of possible tests, including the following:

- see if the coin will actually go through the slot – a test of diameter and thickness

- measure the coin's electrical resistance – coins made of different materials usually have different resistances across their diameters and thicknesses

- compare different coins' speeds at the bottom of the slope – being of differing mass and diameter they will roll down the slope at different speeds

- measure the degree of braking – coins of differing resistance, diameter and thickness will be braked by a magnetic field by different amounts

- measure how high they bounce – different coins will bounce to different heights when they hit a surface (this is a measure of the coefficient of restitution).

Some of these might well make interesting explorations for you. If there is a vending machine manufacturer or supplier near to you, you may be able to go and see the various mechanisms used to find out which coin has been inserted.

Q3

Let 0.03 m be represented by 1.0 cm.

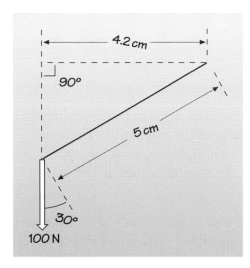

Figure 2.24 Scale diagram of Figure 2.9

The distance representing x measures 4.2 cm, so x is 0.13 m. Therefore the moment of the force is given by

$$100\,N \times 0.13\,m = 13\,N\,m$$

Alternatively, using trigonometry, distance x will be 0.15 m × cos 30°. The moment of the force is then given by

$$100\,N \times 0.15\,m \times \cos 30° = 13\,N\,m$$

(*Note:* Scale diagrams are usually less accurate than trigonometry unless you can work with a large scale.)

Q4

The moment of the force is 170 N m, so

$$170\,N\,m = \text{unknown force} \times 0.42\,m$$

Therefore

$$\text{unknown force} = \frac{170\,N\,m}{0.42\,m}$$
$$= 404.76\,N$$
$$= 4.1 \times 10^2\,N$$
(to two significant figures)

Q5

(a) The moment tending to rotate the fork-lift truck in a clockwise direction is given by

$$220050\,N \times 1.914\,m = 421175.7\,N\,m$$

The moment tending to rotate the fork-lift truck in an anticlockwise direction is given by

$$\text{maximum load} \times 2.10\,m$$

For equilibrium we have

$$\text{maximum load} \times 2.10\,m = 421175.7\,N\,m$$

So

$$\text{maximum load} = \frac{421175.7\,N\,m}{2.10\,m}$$
$$= 200559.9\,N$$
$$= 2.01 \times 10^5\,N$$
(to three significant figures)

or a mass of 2.05×10^4 kg (taking the weight of a 1 kg mass to be 9.8 N).

(b) The shorter the distance from the load on the forks to the front axle (the pivot if it tips up) the smaller will be its anticlockwise moment. Therefore the load can be bigger if this distance is smaller.

Q6

First take moments about the rear axle and then about the front axle.

The sum of the clockwise moments about the rear axle is given by

$$(12000\,N \times 1.50\,m) + (1600\,N \times 2.00\,m)$$
$$= 21200\,N\,m$$

The anticlockwise moment about the rear axle is given by

$$R_2 \times 3.50\,m$$

For equilibrium

$$R_2 \times 3.50\,m = 21200\,N\,m$$

So

$$R_2 = \frac{21200\,\text{N}\,\text{m}}{3.50\,\text{m}}$$

$$= 6057.1\,\text{N}$$

$$= 6.06 \times 10^3 \text{ N or } 6.06\,\text{kN}$$

(to three significant figures)

The sum of the anticlockwise moments about the front axle is given by

$$(12000\,\text{N} \times 2.00\,\text{m}) + (1600\,\text{N} \times 1.50\,\text{m})$$
$$= 26400\,\text{N}\,\text{m}$$

The anticlockwise moment about the front axle is given by

$$R_1 \times 3.50 \text{ m}$$

For equilibrium

$$R_1 \times 3.50\,\text{m} = 26400\,\text{N}\,\text{m}$$

So

$$R_1 = \frac{26400\,\text{N}\,\text{m}}{3.50\,\text{m}}$$

$$= 7542.9\,\text{N}$$

$$= 7.54 \times 10^3 \text{ N or } 7.54\,\text{kN}$$

(to three significant figures)

There is, of course, a quicker way of obtaining R_1 once you have the value of R_2. Think of what the sum of R_1 and R_2 must be equal to – the sum of the weights of the car and its occupants.

Q7

(a) The anticlockwise moment is given by

$$(200\,\text{N} \times 0.20\,\text{m}) + (200\,\text{N} \times 0.20\,\text{m}) = 80\,\text{N}\,\text{m}$$

(b) The anticlockwise moment is given by

$$(200\,\text{N} \times 0.40\,\text{m}) + (200\,\text{N} \times 0\,\text{m}) = 80\,\text{N}\,\text{m}$$

(c) The torque, or moment, of a couple is given by

one force × perpendicular distance
between the forces.

It is a matter of fact that, unfortunately, very large numbers of people are killed or injured on the roads. About 4500 die each year and many tens of thousands are injured. To reduce the likelihood of serious injury, vehicle design has been improved in many ways.

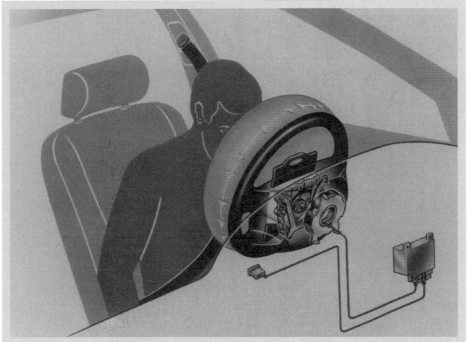

Seatbelts, airbags, collapsible steering columns, dentable windscreens, squashable fascias and squashable front and rear ends have all added to safety, but how? To answer that you will need to recall some GCSE physics and learn more formal ways of expressing it – using equations and graphs. The first few questions in the Ready to Study test are designed to jog your memory. If any of them cause you problems, you will need to get together with other students and your textbooks or your old GCSE notes and do some serious revision.

However, before you check out your knowledge with the Ready to Study test, you should do some research on the latest safety features that car manufacturers are designing into cars. Find out more about how airbags work, what anti-lock brakes are, the value of traction control systems and what crumple zones do. *Which?* reports and *AA Magazine* articles related to car safety, child seats and crash helmets (for bicycles too) are useful sources of information. The Further Reading and Resources section at the end of the unit gives details of some of these. Your teacher may also have some relevant articles you could read, or visit the library and look for some of this information yourself.

3

SAFETY IN CRASHES

Before you begin this section you should be able to:

- distinguish between scalar and vector quantities and give examples
- describe motion in terms of displacement, velocity and acceleration
- use graphical methods to represent displacement, velocity and acceleration
- interpret motion graphs, using terms such as 'rest', 'uniform velocity' and 'acceleration'
- define displacement in terms of average velocity and time taken
- use the equation force = mass × acceleration ($F = ma$)
- draw tangents to curves
- calculate areas under graphs.

QUESTIONS

R1 When motion is described in physics, certain phrases are used with a precise meaning. Explain the meaning of:

(a) at rest

(b) uniform acceleration

(c) negative acceleration.

R2 In physics it is important to know whether a quantity is a scalar or a vector, since scalars and vectors are dealt with in very different ways, particularly when more than one quantity is acting.

Which of the following are vector quantities: force, mass, weight, displacement, work, energy, speed, velocity? Give a reason for your answer.

R3 Study the values below and the graphs in Figures 3.1 and 3.2, and decide how the variables are related. State the relationship between each pair of variables in (a), (b), (c) and (d) and explain how you decided. Assume that both graphs have linear axes.

(a)	x	1	2	3	4	5	6
	y	3	6	9	12	15	18
(b)	a	1	2	3	4	5	6
	b	36	18	12	9	7.2	6

(c) See Figure 3.1.

(d) See Figure 3.2.

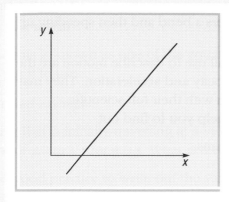 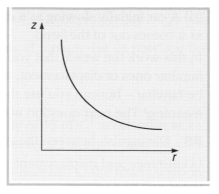

Figure 3.1   **Figure 3.2**

From GCSE science you will remember the link between force, mass and acceleration:

$$\text{force (N)} = \text{mass (kg)} \times \text{acceleration (m s}^{-2})$$

Large forces, accelerating or decelerating, are produced by (or produce) large accelerations and decelerations. Large forces on the human body cause greater damage. Use the expression $F = ma$ to answer the following questions.

R4 If the average acceleration in the initial part of a vehicle collision at 30 mph is 150 m s^{-2}, calculate the average restraining force provided by the occupant's seatbelt. The occupant's mass is 80 kg.

R5 If a seatbelt snaps at around 25 000 N calculate, again for an 80 kg occupant, the largest acceleration that the belt could withstand.

The human body can withstand accelerations of roughly 450 m s^{-2} for 0.04 s, 400 m s^{-2} for 0.1 s and 150 m s^{-2} for 1 s before injury occurs. The problem for vehicle designers is how to reduce the acceleration to as low a value as possible. The following questions involve the calculation of accelerations.

R6 At the instant of lift-off a Space Shuttle of mass 2×10^6 kg weighs approximately 2×10^7 N. If the total thrust provided by its engine and booster rockets is 3×10^7 N, what would be the Space Shuttle's initial acceleration?

R7 Which of the following are accelerating?

(a) A car travelling along a straight road at a constant speed of 30 m s^{-1}.

(b) A car travelling along a straight road and changing its speed from 15 m s^{-1} to 30 m s^{-1}.

(c) A car travelling around a bend at a constant speed of 30 m s^{-1}.

Try the following questions yourself.

In a car crash the vehicle's front end comes to a stop from 13.4 m s^{-1} (30 mph) in 50 ms (i.e. 0.05 s). What is the average acceleration of this part of the vehicle?

$$a = \frac{v-u}{t}$$

$$= \frac{0\,\mathrm{m\,s}^{-1} - 13.4\,\mathrm{m\,s}^{-1}}{0.05\,\mathrm{s}}$$

$$= -268\,\mathrm{m\,s}^{-2}$$

So the average acceleration is -2.7×10^2 m s^{-2} (to two significant figures).

If the vehicle's front was less crushable and so came to a stop in only 20 ms (0.02 s), calculate its new average acceleration.

$$a = \frac{0\,\mathrm{m\,s}^{-1} - 13.4\,\mathrm{m\,s}^{-1}}{0.02\,\mathrm{s}}$$

$$= -670\,\mathrm{m\,s}^{-2}$$

So the average acceleration is -6.7×10^2 m s^{-1} (to two significant figures).

Why is a crushable front end to a vehicle (a) a possible advantage, (b) a possible disadvantage? Explain.

(a) Being more crushable the collision time is longer and so the acceleration smaller. (b) Being more crushable it might also crush the driver and passenger area too.

A vehicle with a crushable front end is unlikely to have a uniform acceleration (negative) in a crash. Why is this?

Vehicles have lots of different components in them, ranging from the massive and strong engine itself to the rather weak bonnet. So, depending on what is being crushed, the time taken to crush it will vary and this in turn will alter the rate of acceleration.

Measuring the accelerations of vehicles and their occupants, particularly in crashes, is quite difficult to do. These factors change very quickly indeed and so need to be filmed at high speed, much higher than is possible with standard movie cameras or camcorders. If they are available, you may see some of this being done on the videos *When it Comes to the Crunch* and *Are Your Children Sitting Safely?*, which were produced by the Consumers' Association. These show car crashes and the testing of child safety seats. You may be able to use a CD-ROM package called *Multimedia Motion,* which includes high-speed film sequences and will allow you to analyse a range of movements, including car, motorcycle and train crashes.

In reality, since most of the motion dealt with in this unit is in a straight line, we could have used 'speed' instead of 'velocity'. However, to emphasize that acceleration involves 'change of velocity', 'velocity' has been used in most cases.

If you can use the *Multimedia Motion* CD-ROM you will find it helpful to analyse a fairly simple movement – a Space Shuttle launch – to begin with. You can do this yourself with the *Multimedia Motion* package, however, to help you appreciate what is being done, copies of the graphs and screen images of this launch are shown and explained in the following section.

The circles on the picture of the shuttle launch in Figure 3.3 show the positions with time of a specific point on the Shuttle. These were added as the movie played, frame by frame. Any point could be chosen – for example, the nose cone of the external fuel tank, the nose cone of one of the solid fuel boosters or the nose cone of the Shuttle itself. The choice is unimportant, but once a point is chosen you must not change it in the middle of the analysis.

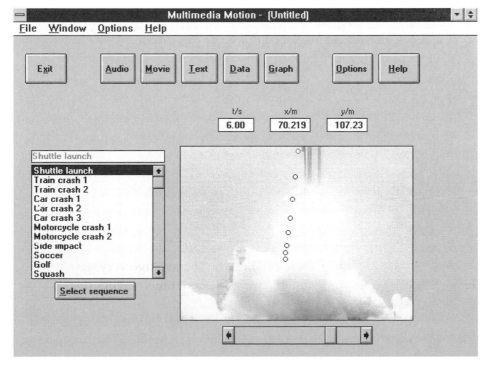

Figure 3.3
Screen image of the launch of the Space Shuttle

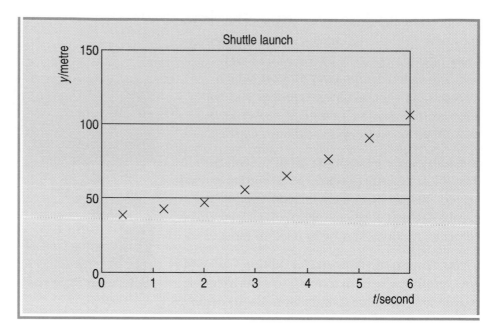

Figure 3.4
Graph of vertical displacement, y, in metres against time, t, in seconds

If you plot the data from the positions, a graph of vertical **displacement**, y, against time, t, appears on the screen, as shown in Figure 3.4.

 Even if you extrapolated back to time zero, this graph would not pass through zero. Explain why this is so.

The point on the Shuttle that was being followed and plotted was not at ground level, even to start with.

Let us now see how the average vertical velocities $v(y)$ are calculated by the computer.

At time 2.8 s the vertical displacement is 55.7 m. At time 4.40 s the vertical displacement is 76.9 m. The average velocity ($v_{average}$) is given by

$$v_{average} = \frac{\text{displacement}}{\text{time taken}}$$

$$= \frac{\Delta x}{\Delta t}$$

where the symbol Δ (the Greek capital letter delta), is used to represent *a change* of displacement or time. So

$$v_{average} = \frac{(76.9\,\text{m} - 55.7\,\text{m})}{(4.4\,\text{s} - 2.8\,\text{s})}$$

$$= 13.25\,\text{ms}^{-1}$$

$$= 13\,\text{ms}^{-1} \text{ (to two significant figures)}$$

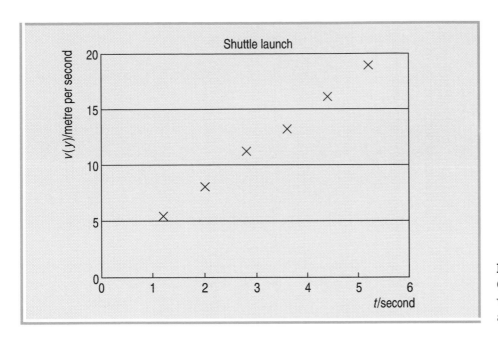

Figure 3.5
Graph of vertical velocity, $v(y)$, against time, t

The middle of that time period is 3.6 s and a velocity $v(y)$ of $13\,\text{m s}^{-1}$ is shown. This agrees well with the screen image of the graph $v(y)$ against time shown in Figure 3.5.

In a similar way, the computer would calculate the other velocities from the values of the displacement and time plots that have been made.

Now for the calculation of acceleration. As you have seen already, two velocities are needed, together with the time taken for these to change. The graph of $v(y)$ against time shows that at a time of 2.8 s the vertical velocity is $11.1\,\text{m s}^{-1}$. At the time of 4.4 s the vertical velocity is $16.0\,\text{m s}^{-1}$. Therefore the average acceleration a_{average} at the middle of this time interval is given by

$$\frac{\text{change of velocity}}{\text{time taken to change}} = \frac{(16.0 - 11.1)\,\text{m s}^{-1}}{(4.4 - 2.8)\,\text{s}}$$

$$= \frac{4.9\,\text{m s}^{-1}}{1.6\,\text{s}}$$

$$= 3.1\,\text{m s}^{-2}$$

The middle of this time interval is 3.6 s and an acceleration $a(y)$ of $3.1\,\text{m s}^{-2}$ is shown on the graph of vertical acceleration, $a(y)$, against time, t, in Figure 3.6 overleaf.

All the velocities and accelerations calculated in this way are being averaged over relatively long time intervals. To obtain what are known as 'instantaneous velocities' and 'instantaneous accelerations' one needs to make the time intervals over which the measurements are made *much* smaller.

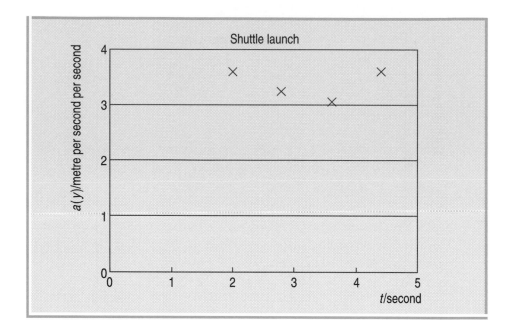

Figure 3.6
Graph of vertical acceleration, $a(y)$, against time, t

Instantaneous velocity $= \dfrac{\text{displacement}}{\text{small time taken}}$

which is also known as 'the rate of change of displacement'.

This is often represented in the form of

$$v_{\text{instantaneous}} = \frac{\delta x}{\delta t}$$

as δt approaches zero.

The symbol δ (the lowercase Greek letter delta), is used to represent a *small change* of displacement or time. You may also have met the calculus method of writing this as

$$v = \frac{\mathrm{d}x}{\mathrm{d}t}$$

The instantaneous acceleration is then given by

$$\text{acceleration}_{\text{instantaneous}} = \frac{\delta v}{\delta t}$$

as δt approaches zero, or, in calculus notation

$$a = \frac{\mathrm{d}v}{\mathrm{d}t}$$

What do you notice about the acceleration of the Shuttle? Is uniform (steady or unchanging) acceleration shown?

No. The graph of $a(y)$ against time in Figure 3.6 shows a changing (non-uniform) acceleration. It varied between approximately 3.6 m s^{-2} and 3.1 m s^{-2}.

 The values of the acceleration after 2.8 s are calculated to have fallen. Why is this unlikely to be true? (*Hint:* Think of what is happening to the mass of the complete spacecraft.)

As the Shuttle takes off it is using up its fuel and so will be getting less massive. Assuming that the thrust is unchanged, this would then result in an increased acceleration.

 What do you think the error in the displayed accelerations might be caused by?

The spacecraft is changing its direction in flight and so the apparent vertical positions and displacements are not true ones. Hence the velocities calculated from these are also untrue.

Now that you are a little familiar with the processes being used by the *Multimedia Motion* package you should get started with the following exploration.

Exploration 3.1 Looking at displacement, velocity and acceleration

Apparatus:

◆ *Multimedia Motion* CD-ROM package
◆ IBM compatible computer running Microsoft Windows

100-120 MINUTES

Get together with other students and share out this exploration. You will probably have to negotiate between yourselves how best to share access to the software and computers. Perhaps give yourselves a week and then pool all your findings and discuss their significance and implications. You must all stick to this deadline or you will be wasting each other's time.

Getting started

Load Windows.

Double click the left-hand mouse button on the *Multimedia Motion* icon.

Double click again on the Space Shuttle icon that appears in the *Multimedia Motion* window.

The introductory screen should then appear accompanied by some music. Following this the Shuttle launch sequence is displayed.

Single click on the HELP button to reveal a contents list.

Move the cursor on to GETTING STARTED; a hand should appear.

Single click again on the left-hand mouse button to reveal a more detailed contents index.

Move the cursor over INTRODUCTION until a hand again appears.

Single click on the mouse to reveal some introductory comments.

Return to the contents index by single clicking on the BACK button.

Single clicking on each of the items in the list will get you information about that item. Much more detailed information is obtained by single clicking the SEARCH button and selecting a topic of your choice. Return to the main screen by single clicking the EXIT button.

If you are used to working within a Microsoft Windows environment, you should find using this software very straightforward indeed.

Part (i)

Use the package to analyse and report on some of the following in terms of displacement, velocity and acceleration:

■ Shuttle launch
■ walking woman
■ jogging woman
■ running woman
■ walking man

- jogging man
- running man
- sprint start
- free fall
- hammer and feather
- helium balloon
- lunar hammer and feather.

To analyse the horizontal motion you will need to plot graphs of horizontal displacement x, horizontal velocity $v(x)$ and horizontal acceleration $a(x)$ – all against time. To analyse vertical motion you will need to plot graphs of vertical displacement y, vertical velocity $v(y)$ and vertical acceleration $a(y)$ – all against time.

Part (ii)

Now select the sequence *Car crash 3* and plot the position of a spot on the dummy's head as the collision takes place. You will probably find it best to do one set of plots as the dummy is moving forwards and another as it rebounds into the seat. Otherwise it is difficult to plot the rebound as the points already plotted obscure the dummy's head.

Obtain graphs of (a) horizontal displacement, x, with time, t, (b) horizontal velocity, $v(x)$, with time, t, and (c) horizontal acceleration, $a(x)$, with time, t. Write a report on how these parameters change during the course of the collision.

Recalling the data on the accelerations that the human body can withstand (namely $450 \ \mathrm{m \ s^{-2}}$ for 0.04 s, $400 \ \mathrm{m \ s^{-2}}$ for 0.1 s and $150 \ \mathrm{m \ s^{-2}}$ for 1 s) would this dummy have been 'killed' by the acceleration alone?

No, the dummy would not have been 'killed', the accelerations are rather low. This should not be too surprising, the dummy was being restrained by a seatbelt.

Part (iii)

Still using the sequence *Car crash 3*, plot the positions of a point on the upright dividing the front and rear doors of the vehicle. As before, obtain graphs of (a) horizontal displacement, x, with time, t, (b) horizontal velocity, $v(x)$, with time, t, and (c) horizontal acceleration, $a(x)$, with time, t. Write a report on how these parameters change during the course of the collision.

How do the accelerations of the dummy and the main body of the car compare? Which had the greatest acceleration?

The dummy underwent the greatest acceleration. Perhaps this seems surprising but it is less so when one considers the need to stop the occupants from hitting the dashboard or windscreen in a relatively short distance.

If you have time you might like to analyse and report on some other crash sequences.

Exploration 3.2 What child safety seats should I recommend?

100-120 MINUTES

Resources:

♦ *Which?* reports ♦ magazine articles ♦ manufacturers' information and relevant books ♦ overhead projector ♦ flipchart or presentation graphics software (e.g. Freelance Graphics, Harvard Graphics or similar) ♦ computer

Imagine that you are responsible for recommending the purchase of a range of child safety seats to be sold in all your company's shops. You wish to ensure that your customers get the best value for money and assurance of these seats' safety.

In order to get your recommendations taken further you need to give a presentation to the directors, backed up by relevant data and, where possible, explanatory detail. In your presentation (to your student colleagues and teaching staff) you could use (i) an overhead projector, (ii) computer presentation graphics, (iii) flipcharts, or a combination of these and other media.

Exploration 3.3 Measuring impact forces

50-60 MINUTES

Apparatus:

♦ dynamics trolley ♦ dummy steering wheel model ♦ runway ♦ brick ♦ sponge ♦ paper ♦ aluminium foil ♦ Sellotape ♦ timing/speed measuring equipment ♦ Plasticine ♦ pencil sharpener (for spike) ♦ newtonmeters (0–10 N and 0–50 N) ♦ thread ♦ ruler

> Runways are often large and can have sharp corners. Care is needed when moving them about.

In a car crash, the driver can be quite badly injured by the steering wheel, if they are not protected by an airbag, seatbelt or collapsible steering column. The force with which the body can hit it can be high enough to damage internal organs.

Get together with other students and share out this exploration of how the impact force is changed by one or more of the following:

(a) hardness of the material hit

(b) having a squashable front end of various lengths and materials

(c) impacting at different speeds

(d) changing the mass of the vehicle.

The equipment should be set up as in Figure 3.7.

As the collision occurs, the dummy impacts on to the spike, which penetrates the Plasticine. To get an indication of the forces required to penetrate in each collision, remould the Plasticine and then pull the dummy on to the spike using a thread attached to a newtonmeter (see Figure 3.8). Record this penetration force for each type of collision.

Report on what you did and what your findings were to the rest of your group.

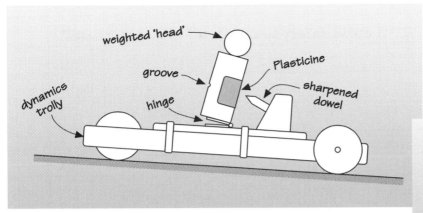

Figure 3.7   Arrangement of apparatus for Exploration 3.3

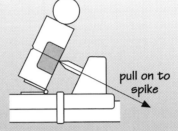

Figure 3.8
Pulling the dummy on
to the spike

Graph work: on the slopes

Velocities and accelerations can also be calculated from the slopes of graphs by drawing tangents to the curves at the required points. A possible graph of passenger displacement with time during a 30 mph (13.4 m s^{-1}) impact might look like that shown in Figure 3.9 overleaf.

To find the instantaneous velocity of the passenger as the vehicle rebounds from the crash, first draw a tangent to the curve at the 100 ms point as shown in Figure 3.9. To ease your calculation, this tangent has been made long enough to just touch the 75 ms and 125 ms lines. A right-angled triangle ABC has also been drawn with sides parallel to the vertical and horizontal axes. The 'change of displacement' is given by the length of side AB, and the 'time taken to change' by the length of side BC. The instantaneous velocity $v_{\text{instantaneous}}$ is then given by

$$v_{\text{instantaneous}} = \frac{\text{change of displacement (AB)}}{\text{time taken to change (BC)}}$$

$$= \frac{\Delta x}{\Delta t}$$

Therefore

$$v_{\text{instantaneous}} = \frac{1.275\,\text{m} - 0.950\,\text{m}}{0.050\,\text{s}}$$

$$= \frac{0.325\,\text{m}}{0.050\,\text{s}}$$

$$= 6.5\,\text{m s}^{-1}$$

(*Note:* To obtain an answer in m s^{-1} the 50 ms must be converted into 0.050 s.)

Compare this with the velocity–time graph for the passenger (Figure 3.10) at that same instant of time. It should also give a value of 6.5 m s^{-1}.

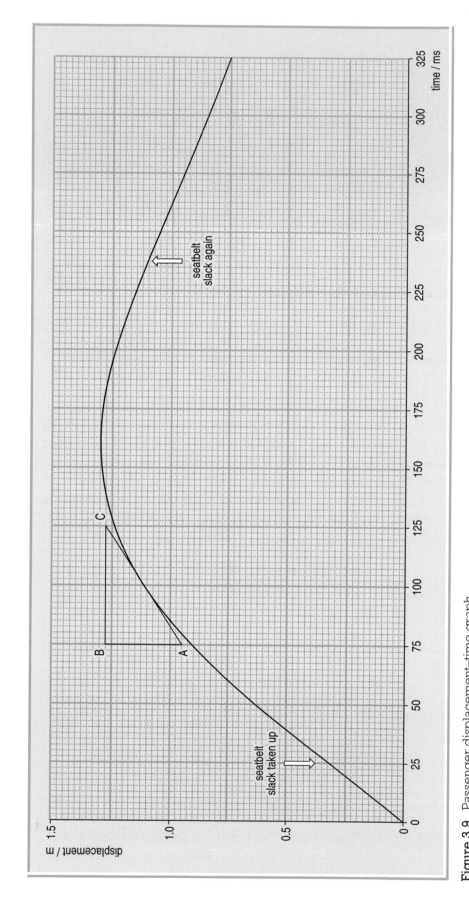

Figure 3.9 Passenger displacement–time graph
(adapted from Macmillan, R. M. (1984) 'Studying vehicle collisions', *Physics Bulletin*, vol. 35, no. 7)

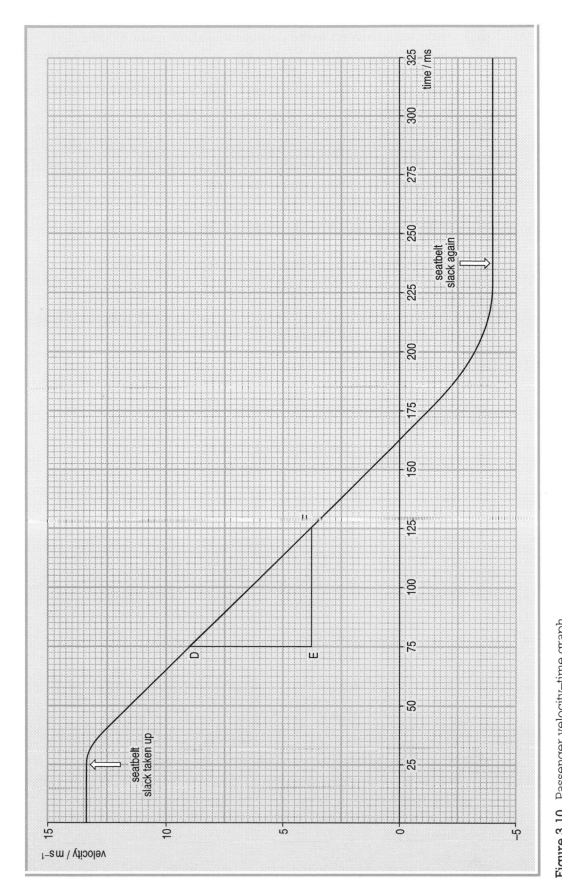

Figure 3.10 Passenger velocity–time graph
(adapted from Macmillan, R. M. (1984) 'Studying vehicle collisions', *Physics Bulletin*, vol. 35, no. 7)

By drawing tangents to the displacement–time graph (Figure 3.9), calculate the instantaneous velocities of the passenger at (a) 12.5 ms, (b) 275 ms and (c) when the displacement is a maximum. Compare your results with the velocity–time graph (Figure 3.10) – the values should agree fairly well. Use a thin plane mirror across the line to help you draw tangents. When the curve and its image appear to be continuous, the mirror is at right angles to the line. If you mark the mirror's position it is then easy to mark the tangent, which will be at right angles to it and touching the curve.

(a) 13.4 m s^{-1}, (b) -4.0 m s^{-1} and (c) 0 m s^{-1}.

The same technique will enable you to calculate the accelerations involved in this crash from the velocity–time graph (Figure 3.10). Again, a tangent was drawn to the 'curve' at a time of 100 ms. This tangent lies along the line itself as the 'curve' here is a straight line. It was made long enough to just touch the 75 ms and 125 ms lines.

A right-angled triangle DEF was completed with sides parallel to the horizontal and vertical axes. The 'change of velocity' is then given by the length of side DE and the 'time taken to change' by the length of side EF. The instantaneous acceleration $a_{instantaneous}$ is then given by

$$a_{instantaneous} = \frac{\text{change of velocity (DE)}}{\text{time taken to change (EF)}}$$

$$= \frac{\Delta v}{\Delta t}$$

Therefore

$$a_{instantaneous} = \frac{(3.75 - 9.0)\,\text{ms}^{-1}}{0.050\,\text{s}}$$

$$= \frac{-5.25\,\text{ms}^{-1}}{0.050\,\text{s}}$$

$$= -105\,\text{ms}^{-2}$$

$$= -1.1 \times 10^2\,\text{ms}^{-2} \text{ (to two significant figures)}$$

 What does the negative sign indicate in the above?

The negative sign indicates the direction of the acceleration. As the passenger started with a positive velocity this acceleration will slow them down.

 By drawing tangents to the velocity–time graph, calculate the instantaneous accelerations of the passenger at (a) 12.5 ms and (b) 200 ms.

(a) 0 m s^{-2}, (b) approximately -62 m s^{-2}.

In reality the accelerations of the driver and passenger are often much greater than those you have calculated. This is because the graphs are not as smooth as those provided and really have lots of humps and bumps in them.

Graph work: under the slopes

At the beginning of this section we looked at the first of the equations of motion: $v = u + at$. There are two other equations of motion that are easily derived with the aid of graphs in the following questions.

 Figure 3.11 shows a velocity–time graph of a racing car travelling at a constant velocity of 50 m s^{-1} for 10.0 s.

(a) At this steady velocity what displacement would have taken place in the 10.0 s?

(b) Calculate the area under this line graph using the units of this graph. What do you notice about your answers to parts (a) and (b)?

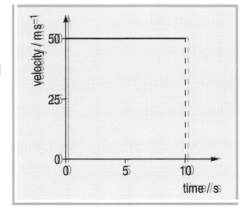

Figure 3.11

(a) Displacement = average velocity × time taken.

So

$$displacement = 50ms^{-1} \times 10.0s$$
$$= 500m$$

(b) The area under the line graph represents 50 m s^{-1} × 10.0 s, so it is also 500 m.

 Figure 3.12 shows a velocity–time graph of a racing car accelerating from 0 m s^{-1} to 50 m s^{-1} in 10.0 s.

(a) Using the formula

$$average\ velocity = \frac{u + v}{2}$$

calculate the car's average velocity over the 10.0 s.

(b) Using this average velocity, calculate the displacement of this car over the 10.0 s.

(c) Calculate the area under the line graph shown in Figure 3.12 using the units of this graph. What do you notice about your answers to parts (b) and (c)?

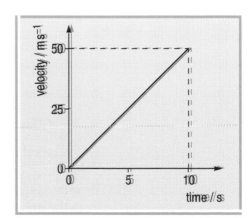

Figure 3.12

(a) 25 m s^{-1}.

(b)

Displacement = average velocity × time taken

$$= 25\,\text{ms}^{-1} \times 10.0\,\text{s}$$

$$= 250\,\text{m}$$

(c) The area under the line graph represents $^1/_2 \times 50$ m s^{-1} × 10.0, so it is also 250 m.

 Figure 3.13 shows a car accelerating from 25 m s^{-1} to 50 m s^{-1} in 10.0s.

(a) What is this car's average velocity over the 10.0 s?

(b) Using this average velocity, calculate its displacement over the 10.0 s.

(c) Calculate the *total* area under the line graph using the units of this graph. (You will need to find the areas of both the triangular and rectangular sections.) What do you notice about your answers to (b) and (c)?

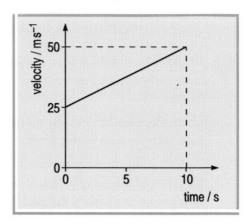

Figure 3.13

(a) 37.5 m s^{-1} or 38 m s^{-1} to two significant figures.

(b)

Displacement = average velocity × time taken

$$= 37.5\,\text{ms}^{-1} \times 10.0\,\text{s}$$

$$= 375\,\text{m}$$

(c) Area of rectangular section is

$25\,\text{ms}^{-1} \times 10.0\,\text{s} = 250\,\text{m}$

Area of triangular section is

$\dfrac{1}{2} \times 25\,\text{ms}^{-1} \times 10.0\,\text{s} = 125\,\text{m}$

So total displacement is 375 m. The same value as obtained in (b).

By now you should have realized that the displacement can be calculated from the area under a velocity–time graph. This is in fact generally the case, regardless of the shape of the graph and the type of motion – uniform or not. The following argument will show you why this is so.

The first shaded section of the graph in Figure 3.14 is of a *very* small time interval δt_1. Over this time the velocity can be considered to remain

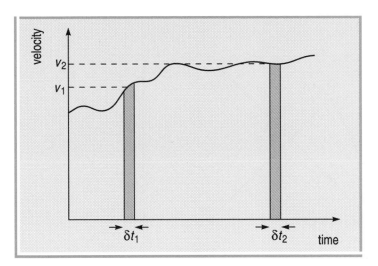

Figure 3.14
Velocity–time graph of non-uniform motion

constant at δv_1. Since displacement is given by 'average velocity × time taken', then

$$\text{displacement } s_1 = v_1 \times \delta t_1$$

On the graph this is very nearly the area of the first shaded section. The smaller the time interval considered, the nearer the velocity will be to a constant value.

By a similar argument you should be able to see that the displacement in time δt_2 is given by the second shaded section. So, over the whole of the time period for which the graph is drawn the total displacement would be given by the summation of the areas of lots of adjacent sections of width δt_1, δt_2, δt_3 ... The result would be the whole area under the graph.

Try the following questions to reassure yourself of the technique.

Q1 Using the velocity–time graph shown in Figure 3.15, calculate the displacement after 5.0 s. ◆

Q2 Using the velocity–time graph shown in Figure 3.16, calculate the displacement over the time period 1.0 s to 6.0 s. ◆

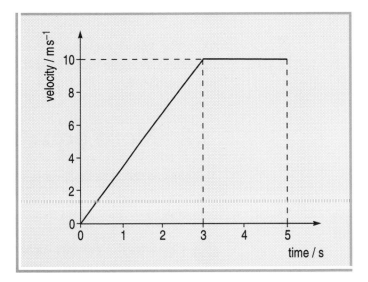

Figure 3.15

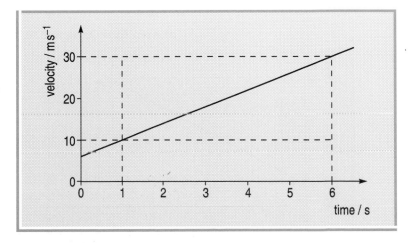

Figure 3.16

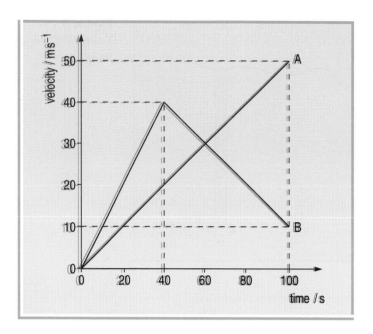

Figure 3.17
Velocity–time graph
for two vehicles

Q3 The velocity–time graph in Figure 3.17 shows two vehicles, A and B, travelling along the same route. Which vehicle is ahead after 100 s and by how much? ◆

3.2 More equations of motion

Analysis of the area under a velocity–time graph can also help us to derive another of the equations of motion. Work your way through the following question.

 Consider the velocity–time graph shown in Figure 3.18 for a vehicle that has accelerated uniformly from velocity u to velocity v in a time t.

(a) Write an expression for the displacement s after time t in terms of u, v and t.

(b) Knowing that

$$a = \frac{v - u}{t}$$

so that

$$v = u + at$$

rewrite your expression in (a) in terms of a, s, t and u.

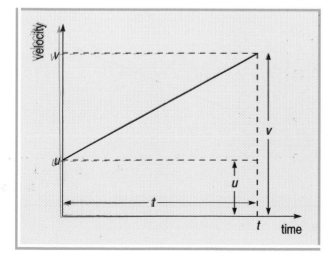

Figure 3.18

(a) You need to sum the area under the line graph. The area of the rectangle is

$u \times t$

The area of the triangle is

$$\frac{1}{2}(v-u) \times t$$

Therefore

$$s = ut + \frac{1}{2}(v-u) \times t \tag{3.1}$$

(b) Substituting for v in Equation (3.1), where $v = u + at$, we get

$$s = ut + \frac{1}{2}(u + at - u) \times t$$

$$= ut + \frac{1}{2}(at) \times t$$

$$= ut + \frac{1}{2}at^2$$

You now have a second equation of motion

$$s = ut + \frac{1}{2}at^2$$

To get to another one of the equations of motion will take us rather longer. We begin by looking at that last case another way, starting from the relationship:

displacement = average velocity × time taken $\tag{3.2}$

Look at Figure 3.18 once more. During the time t the average velocity is given by

$$\text{average velocity} = \frac{u+v}{2}$$

so substituting $\dfrac{u+v}{2}$ in Equation (3.2) gives

$$s = \left(\frac{u+v}{2}\right)t \tag{3.3}$$

But

$$v = u + at$$

so by rearranging this equation we get

$$at = v - u$$

and

$$t = \left(\frac{v-u}{a}\right)$$

Substituting now for t in Equation (3.3) we get

$$s = \left(\frac{u+v}{2}\right) \times \left(\frac{v-u}{a}\right)$$

Expanding this we get

$$s = \frac{\left(v^2 - u^2\right)}{2a}$$

Multiplying both sides of this equation by $2a$ we get

$$2a \times s = \frac{\left(v^2 - u^2\right)}{2a} \times 2a$$

so

$$2as = v^2 - u^2$$

More usually, this is given as

$$v^2 = u^2 + 2as$$

There is actually another equation of motion

$$s = vt - \frac{1}{2}at^2$$

but it is rarely included. The complete list of the equations of motion for uniform accelerated motion is shown in the box. Do remember that these equations hold true *only* for uniformly accelerated motion.

EQUATIONS OF MOTION FOR UNIFORM ACCELERATED MOTION

$v = u + at$

$s = ut + \frac{1}{2}at^2$

$v^2 = u^2 + 2as$

$s = ut - \frac{1}{2}at^2$

where u is the initial velocity in m s^{-1}, v is the final velocity in m s^{-1}, a is the acceleration in m s^{-2}, t is the time taken in seconds and s is the displacement in metres.

Have a go at some, or all, of the following set of questions to gain familiarity with the use of the equations of motion. Again an example has been provided to remind you of a sensible layout.

Worked example

A cyclist accelerates from rest (0 m s^{-1}) at a rate of 2.0 m s^{-2} for 5.0 s. What is the cyclist's displacement after that time?

$a = 2.0$ m s^{-2}, $s = ?$, $t = 5.0$ s, $u = 0$ m s^{-1}

Using

$$s = ut + \frac{1}{2}at^2$$

we have

$$s = \left(0\,\text{ms}^{-1} \times 5.0\,\text{s}\right) + \frac{1}{2}\left[2.0\,\text{ms}^{-2} \times \left(5.0\,\text{s}\right)^2\right]$$
$$= 0 + 25\,\text{m}$$
$$= 25\,\text{m}$$

So the total displacement is 25 m. ◆

Michael Rosswess, sprinter

Q4 (a) A 100 m sprinter has an initial rate of acceleration of 6.0 m s^{-2} for the first 1.0 s of the run. What is the sprinter's displacement at the end of the first second?

(b) If this same sprinter was able to keep up this rate of acceleration for the whole 100 m, what velocity would have been attained at the finish?

(c) At this same rate of acceleration, how long would this 100 m run take the sprinter?

Needless to say, you should find that neither of your answers to (b) or (c) could be achieved in reality. ◆

Q5 The Ford Mondeo 2.0 Ghia is quoted by a car magazine as being able to accelerate from 30 mph (13.4 m s^{-1}) to 70 mph (31.3 m s^{-1}) in 9.2 s. For the sake of simplicity, assume that this acceleration is uniform and taking place on a straight road.

Ford Mondeo 2.0 Ghia

(a) Calculate the acceleration in m s^{-2}.

(b) How far would the car have travelled in metres whilst accelerating at this rate? ◆

Achievements

After working through this section you should be able to:

- use the terms 'average' and 'instantaneous' when applied to speed/velocity and acceleration

- use the slope of a tangent to find instantaneous velocity from a displacement–time graph or instantaneous acceleration from a velocity–time graph

- use the symbol Δ for a change in a quantity, as in Δs, Δt, and the symbol δ for a small change in a quantity, as in δs, δt

- determine displacement by calculating the area under a velocity–time graph

- derive three equations of motion for uniformly accelerated motion in a straight line

$$v = u + at$$

$$s = ut + \frac{1}{2}at^2$$

$$v^2 = u^2 + 2as$$

and state the fourth

$$s = vt - \frac{1}{2}at^2$$

- use these equations to solve problems.

Glossary

Acceleration   Unit: metre per second per second (m s^{-2}). The rate of change of velocity. Acceleration is most commonly thought of in terms of an increase in speed and deceleration a decrease in speed, though this ignores the fact that direction is also involved. An object rotating at constant speed in a circle is still accelerating. Instantaneous accelerations are those measured over very small time intervals. Acceleration is a vector quantity.

Displacement   Unit: metre (m). This is the distance moved in a stated direction. Displacement is a vector quantity.

Speed   See *velocity*.

Uniformly accelerated motion   Motion in which the velocity of an object changes by equal amounts in equal times. It is usually brought about by the action of a constant net force on an object of fixed mass.

Velocity   Unit: metre per second (m s^{-1}). The rate of change of displacement. Velocity is a vector quantity. It is not the same as speed as the latter does not take account of direction and so is not a vector quantity. Instantaneous velocities are those measured over small time intervals.

Answers to Ready to Study test

R1

(a) Not moving at all, velocity $v = 0$ (the value of displacement s will not necessarily be zero).

(b) The value of acceleration a is constant, e.g. $a = 5\ \text{m s}^{-2}$. Uniform is taken to mean not changing.

(c) Acceleration is a vector quantity and the negative sign is used to show the direction of the acceleration. Don't confuse it with deceleration. A negative acceleration will make an object go faster if it already has a negative velocity!

R2

Force, weight, displacement and velocity are vector quantities. This is because they all have direction as well as magnitude.

R3

(a) When y is plotted against x a straight-line graph results, showing direct proportion $y = 3x$.

(b) When b is plotted against $\frac{1}{a}$ a straight-line graph results, showing inverse proportion $b = \frac{36}{a}$.

(c) Figure 3.1 shows a linear relationship of the type $y = mx + c$.

(d) You can't tell what the relationship shown in Figure 3.2 is without numbers.

It could be $z = \frac{k}{r^2}$.

R4

$F = ma$

so

$$F = 80\,\text{kg} \times 150\,\text{ms}^{-2}$$

$$= 12000\,\text{N}$$

$$= 1.2 \times 10^4\,\text{N}$$

This is near the weight of an average family car!

R5

$F = ma$

so

$$a = \frac{F}{m}$$

and

$$a = \frac{25000\,\text{N}}{80\,\text{kg}}$$

$$= 312.5\,\text{ms}^{-2}$$

$$= 3.1 \times 10^2\,\text{ms}^{-2} \text{ (to two significant figures)}$$

As this is in the opposite direction to the velocity this gives us

$a = -3.1 \times 10^2\,\text{m s}^{-2}$

(*Note:* The negative sign shows the direction of the acceleration, and does not necessarily mean that it is a deceleration – see the answer to R1(c).)

R6

$$\text{Resultant force} = \left(3 \times 10^7 - 2 \times 10^7\right)\text{N}$$

$$= 1 \times 10^7\,\text{N}$$

So, as $F = ma$ we have

$1 \times 10^7\,\text{N} = 2 \times 10^6\,\text{kg} \times a$

giving

$$a = \frac{1 \times 10^7\,\text{N}}{2 \times 10^6\,\text{kg}}$$

$$= 5\,\text{ms}^{-2}$$

The actual acceleration is in fact a little smaller than this. The data above have been approximated to make them simple to deal with.

R7

(a) No acceleration.

(b) This car is accelerating: although its direction is unchanged, its speed is changing.

(c) This car is accelerating: although its speed is unchanged, its direction is changing.

(d) This car is accelerating: both its speed and direction are changing.

R8

(a) Distance is a scalar quantity used to describe the length of a journey whereas displacement is a vector quantity and represents the change in position, this includes direction and distance away from a defined point. You can take a journey of a great distance and end up where you started, i.e. with no displacement.

(b) Speed is a scalar quantity. It is the rate of change of distance travelled with time. Velocity is the speed in a given direction and as such is a vector quantity.

(c) These are both velocities with the same speed but in opposite directions. The positive direction can often be taken to be along the x-axis. At other times it is important to define your positive for displacement and to use that as the positive direction for the velocity and the acceleration.

(d) These are both accelerations of the same value but acting in opposite directions. Positive accelerations will act in the same direction as the positive displacement direction. Negative acceleration will act in the opposite direction to the positive displacement direction.

The effect of these accelerations will depend on the motion at the start. Let's imagine that

you are backing a car into a garage with velocity -0.2 m s^{-1} and each acceleration is applied to it. If the positive direction of displacement is out of the garage. Then $a = +3$ m s^{-2} will act in the direction out of the garage, and therefore slow down the car, but the negative acceleration would make the speed increase. Bad news for the back wall of the garage.

R9

See Figure 3.19. Discuss your answers with other students explaining, with calculations, the shapes of the graphs.

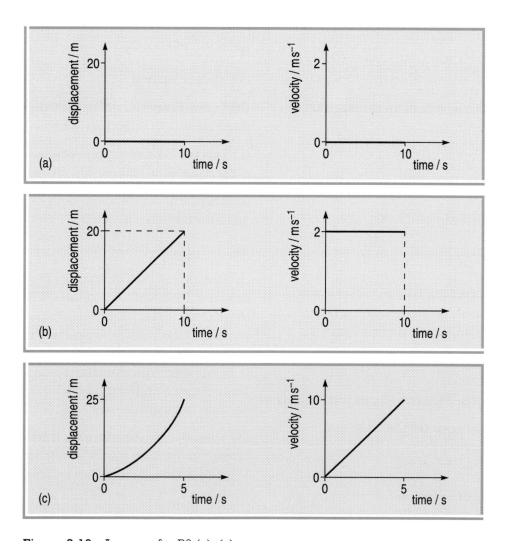

Figure 3.19 Answers for R9 (a)–(c)

R10

(a) Displacement = velocity × time

(b)

$s = 5\,\text{s} \times 20\,\text{ms}^{-1}$

$\quad = 100\,\text{m}$

$\quad = 1 \times 10^2\,\text{m}$

(c)

$$\text{Acceleration} = \frac{\text{change of velocity}}{\text{time taken to change}}$$

Answers to questions in the text

Q1

You should have summed the areas of the triangular and rectangular sections. Area of triangular section is

$\frac{1}{2} \times 10\,\text{m}\,\text{s}^{-1} \times 3.0\,\text{s} = 15\,\text{m}$

Area of rectangular section is

$10\,\text{m}\,\text{s}^{-1} \times 2.0\,\text{s} = 20\,\text{m}$

So total displacement is 35 m.

Q2

Be careful here. Only calculate the area below the graph line, nothing beyond the line at all. You should have summed the areas of the triangular and rectangular sections again.

Area of rectangular section is

$10\,\text{m}\,\text{s}^{-1} \times 5.0\,\text{s} = 50\,\text{m}$

Area of triangular section is

$\frac{1}{2} \times 20\,\text{m}\,\text{s}^{-1} \times 5.0\,\text{s} = 50\,\text{m}$

So displacement is 100 m.

Q3

For vehicle A you just need to calculate the area of the large triangle:

$\frac{1}{2} \times 50\,\text{ms}^{-1} \times 100\,\text{s} = 2500\,\text{m}$

$\qquad\qquad = 2.5 \times 10^3\,\text{m} \text{ or } 2.5\,\text{km}$

For vehicle B you need to sum the areas of two triangles and one rectangle.

First triangle:

$\frac{1}{2} \times 40\,\text{m}\,\text{s}^{-1} \times 40\,\text{s} = 800\,\text{m}$

Second triangle:

$\frac{1}{2} \times 30\,\text{m}\,\text{s}^{-1} \times 60\,\text{s} = 900\,\text{m}$

Rectangle:

$10\,\text{m}\,\text{s}^{-1} \times 60\,\text{s} = 600\,\text{m}$

Therefore for vehicle B

$\text{total displacement} = 800\,\text{m} + 900\,\text{m} + 600\,\text{m}$

$\qquad\qquad\qquad = 2300\,\text{m}$

$\qquad\qquad\qquad = 2.3 \times 10^3\,\text{m} \text{ or } 2.3\,\text{km}$

So vehicle A is ahead by 200 m or $2.0 \times 10^2\,\text{m}$.

Q4

(a) $a = 6.0\,\text{m}\,\text{s}^{-2}$, $s = ?$, $t = 1.0\,\text{s}$, $u = 0\,\text{m}\,\text{s}^{-1}$

Using

$s = ut + \frac{1}{2}at^2$

you should have

$s = (0 \times 1.0\,\text{s}) + \frac{1}{2}\left[6.0\,\text{ms}^{-2} \times (1.0\,\text{s})^2\right]$

$\quad = 3.0\,\text{m}$

(b) $a = 6.0\,\text{m}\,\text{s}^{-2}$, $s = 100\,\text{m}$, $u = 0\,\text{m}\,\text{s}^{-1}$, $v = ?$

Using

$v^2 = u^2 + 2as$

you should have

$$v^2 = 0^2 + 2(6.0 \text{ m s}^{-2} \times 100 \text{ m})$$

So

$$v^2 = 1200 \text{ m}^2 \text{ s}^{-2}$$

and so

$$v = \sqrt{1200 \text{ m}^2 \text{ s}^{-2}}$$

$$= 35 \text{ ms}^{-1}$$

(c) $a = 6.0 \text{ ms}^{-2}$, $t = ?$, $u = 0 \text{ ms}^{-1}$, $v = 34.64 \text{ ms}^{-1}$

Using

$$v = u + at$$

you should have

$$34.64 \text{ m s}^{-1} = 0 + (6.0 \text{ m s}^{-2} \times t)$$

so

$$t = \frac{34.64 \text{ ms}^{-1}}{6.0 \text{ ms}^{-2}}$$

$$= 5.77 \text{ s}$$

$$= 5.8 \text{ s (to two significant figures)}$$

A world record!

Q5

(a) $a = ?$, $t = 9.2 \text{ s}$, $u = 13.4 \text{ m s}^{-1}$, $v = 31.3 \text{ m s}^{-1}$

Using

$$v = u + at$$

you should have

$$31.3 \text{ m s}^{-1} = 13.4 \text{ m s}^{-1} + (a \times 9.2 \text{ s})$$

So

$$a = \frac{\left(31.3 \text{ ms}^{-1} - 13.4 \text{ ms}^{-1}\right)}{9.2 \text{ s}}$$

$$= 1.95 \text{ ms}^{-2}$$

$$= 2.0 \text{ ms}^{-2} \text{ (to two significant figures)}$$

(b) $a = 1.95 \text{ m s}^{-2}$, $s = ?$, $t = 9.2 \text{ s}$, $u = 13.4 \text{ m s}^{-1}$

Using

$$s = ut + \frac{1}{2}at^2$$

you should have

$$s = \left(13.4 \text{ ms}^{-1} \times 9.2 \text{ s}\right) + \frac{1}{2}\left[1.95 \text{ ms}^{-2} \times \left(9.2 \text{ s}\right)^2\right]$$

$$= 123.28 \text{ m} + 82.52 \text{ m}$$

$$= 205.80 \text{ m}$$

$$= 2.1 \times 10^2 \text{ m (to two significant figures)}$$

You may already be familiar with Newton's laws of motion from your GCSE work. This section focuses mainly on his second law, but is a good place to look at all three.

Sir Isaac Newton's three laws of motion have been fundamental to the development of physics for more than 300 years, and they still describe how things move in today's world.

READY TO STUDY TEST

Before you begin this section you should be able to:

- draw diagrams of objects showing the forces acting on them, including free-body force diagrams
- define equilibrium as the condition when all the forces acting on a body balance each other, i.e. when the resultant force is zero
- use the expression

  work done (J) = force (N) × distance (m)
- use the law of conservation of energy
- describe motion in terms of displacement, velocity and acceleration
- use the expression

  force (N) = mass (kg) × acceleration (m s^{-2})
- define linear momentum and give its unit of measurement.

QUESTIONS

R1 (a) What is the work done if a shopping trolley is pushed with a 50 N force for a distance of 15 m?

(b) If another trolley was pushed over the same distance and only 400 J of energy were transferred, what was the size of the steady force that caused this?

R2 A shopper commented that it was a waste of time buying all this food when the energy it gives us is wasted and disappears in pushing trolleys around the shop. Using your understanding of physics, what are your thoughts on this?

R3 Describe the journey of a bus from one bus stop to the next, in terms of:

(a) distance travelled   (c) its velocity

(b) displacement from its terminal   (d) its acceleration.

R4 What is the force that a 60 kg sprinter generates if at the very start of a race they can accelerate at 8.0 m s^{-2}?

R5 (a) What is linear momentum?   (b) What are its units?

NEWTON'S LAWS OF MOTION   MOMENTUM AND

4.1 Newton's first law of motion

In your GCSE science or physics course you will have met Newton's first law of motion – the one that does not initially appear to be common sense. It states that:

Every object remains at rest or in *uniform motion in a straight line* unless acted upon by an unbalanced force.

The words in italics often comes as a surprise to younger students, who tend to think that things move only when they are being pushed or pulled. Indeed, this was the generally accepted view until the work of Galileo and Newton in the seventeenth century.

Pause for a while and discuss Newton's first law of motion with other students.

- Suggest some examples that clearly illustrate the first law and others where you don't think it works.

- Examine your examples – with another student if possible.

- Look at a textbook for other examples and applications of this law.

NEWTON'S FIRST LAW OF MOTION

Every object remains at rest or in uniform motion in a straight line unless acted upon by an unbalanced force.

4.2 Newton's first law of motion – an alternative approach

Read through the actions described in points 1 to 5 and discuss the answers to questions (a) to (e) with other students.

1 A piece of furniture being pushed across the room.

2 A garden roller being pulled across a lawn.

3 A small boat being pulled with a rope across a stretch of shallow water.

4 A loaded shopping trolley being pushed around a supermarket.

5 A lorry towing a heavy trailer.

(a) What is happening to the objects described as a result of the push or pull?

(b) What will happen to the objects if we stop pushing or pulling them?

(c) Is the push or pull described the only force acting on each object?

(d) Write down two other forces acting on the moving objects.

(e) Which one of these objects will behave in a significantly different manner to the others when we stop pushing or pulling it? Explain.

Exploration 4.1 Motion on an air track

30-40 MINUTES

Apparatus:

◆ linear air track, vehicle and accessories ◆ air blower

Give the vehicle an initial push along the track with no air cushion and watch how it moves subsequently (on its own).

Answer these questions.

1 Is there a force pushing the vehicle along whilst it is moving?

2 Is there a force slowing it down whilst it is moving?

3 Name the forces that you have identified in questions 1 and 2.

4 Say whether each of these is small or large and give your reasons.

Now repeat the experiment but this time with an air cushion from the blower.

Answer these questions.

1 Is there a force pushing the vehicle along whilst it is moving?

2 What force does the air cushion reduce to very low value?

3 What effect does this have on how quickly the vehicle slows down and stops?

Now imagine that we could reduce the force of friction to zero and have an infinitely long air track.

Answer these questions.

1 Would there be a force keeping the vehicle moving or slowing it down?

2 Would the velocity of the vehicle ever change?

3 Would it ever stop moving? (*Hint:* Would it ever slow down?)

Q1 In the light of the results of your investigation try to explain situations 1–5 by answering questions (a)–(e) below.

1 A billiard ball rolling across the table after being hit.

2 A football rolling along the ground after being kicked.

3 A tennis ball at Wimbledon flying through the air.

4 The trolley on the air track moving after it has been pushed.

5 A spacecraft moving halfway between the Earth and Mars.

Questions

(a) Is the force that pushed all the above objects to begin with and started them moving still acting on them?

(b) Which ones will eventually come to rest and why?

(c) Which ones will continue to travel at a constant velocity until an unbalanced force acts on them?

(d) Is there an unbalanced force acting on objects travelling at a constant velocity?

(e) What is true about all the forces on a car (produced by the engine or otherwise) if it is travelling at a constant velocity? ◆

Newton summarised these ideas in this, his first law of motion:

> Every object remains at rest or in *uniform motion in a straight line* unless acted upon by an unbalanced force.

4.3 Newton's second law of motion

In the Ready to Study test you were reminded of the relationship between force, mass and acceleration. Namely that

force (N) = mass (kg) × acceleration (m s^{-2})

or

$$F = ma$$

To produce a non-zero acceleration the force(s) need to be unbalanced.

This relationship was initially established by Isaac Newton, but he did not write it in this form. He used $\dfrac{(v-u)}{\delta t}$ in place of a and obtained

$$F = m\frac{(v-u)}{\delta t}$$
$$= \frac{(mv - mu)}{\delta t}$$

where mv is the final **momentum**, mu is the initial momentum and δt the small time for which the force F is applied. The momentum of an object is the product of its mass and its velocity.

This equation represents Newton's second law of motion, which can be written in words as:

> Force equals the rate of change of momentum.

You should try to remember this.

NEWTON'S SECOND LAW OF MOTION

Force equals the rate of change of momentum.

This law holds true even in relativistic situations where speeds approaching that of light occur and the masses of objects change.

Often the above expression is rearranged in the form

$$F\delta t = mv - mu$$

Fδt (the product of the force and the time for which it acts) is called the **impulse**. As you would expect, the right-hand side of the expression is called the *change of momentum*.

 (a) Since momentum is the product of mass and velocity, what must its units be?

(b) Since impulse is the product of force and the time for which it acts, what must its units be?

(c) What can you say about the units of momentum and those of impulse?

(a) kg m s^{-1}

(b) N s.

(c) They must be equivalent to each other.

Q2 (a) What is the value of the impulse produced by a force of 5.0 N acting for 2.0 s?

(b) What change of momentum would this impulse produce? ◆

Q3 (a) If a car of mass 1000 kg increased its velocity by 10 m s^{-1}, what change of momentum would have occurred to it?

(b) What impulse would have produced this momentum change? ◆

In each of these two questions you should have had numerically identical answers for parts (a) and (b). You could also have used the same units in each case, although it is more common to use 'kg m s^{-1}' for 'change of momentum' and 'N s' for 'impulse'. Do note that 'N s' stands for a 'newton second' and *not* 'newtons'.

Q4 Two identical test cars are crashed at 30 mph (13.4 m s^{-1}) into a wall. The first 'driver' is a dummy of mass 75 kg restrained by a seatbelt. The second 'driver' is an identical dummy, but is not restrained.

(a) What is the change of momentum of each dummy after the crash?

(b) What, therefore, must be the impulse on each dummy as a result of the crash?

(c) The seatbelt, in stretching, brings the first dummy to a stop in 200 ms. What is the average force exerted on it in the collision?

(d) The dummy without a seatbelt is brought to a stop by a collision with the steering wheel in 2.0 ms. What is the average force exerted on it in the collision? ◆

SOME LIGHT-HEARTED REVISION: NEWTON'S BIG IDEAS (CIRCA 1666)

Newton's First Big Idea seems rather obvious. If an object is just sitting around, minding its own business, or even travelling along at a steady pace, nothing will change this state of affairs until something else comes along to change the situation (you don't say?)

His Second Big Idea says that force, as such, is something that causes a body to move. I have actually proved this. Try lying down and see what force it takes to get up again.

The Third Big Idea states that for every action there is an equal and opposite reaction. Therefore, if you kick your dog it will usually bite your ankle … or to be serious (for once), the power coming out of the back end of a rocket will make it go the other way.

Having worked all this out, our Newton decided to have a rest from thinking and went to sit in his backyard. Now if you or I had seen that apple falling from a tree we'd have either ignored it or eaten it. Not our Isaac! He wondered why it had fallen downwards (silly man) and gradually realized that it must have had something pushing or pulling it and that the Moon orbits the Earth held by the same force. From this he deduced that all bodies (or apples) in the Universe are affected by a force varying inversely with the distance between them. He called this force — all together now — gravity and at a single stroke did away once and for all with that old rubbish which declared that stars were moved by devils or angels.

Source: Farman, J. (1991)
A Suspiciously Simple History of Science and Invention. Piccadilly Press, London.

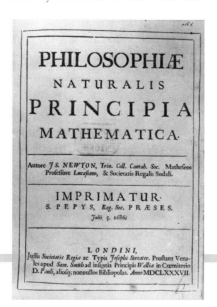

4.4 Investigating momentum

Isaac Newton defined momentum on the very first page of *Principia Mathematica* as (translated from the original Latin):

> The quantity of motion [our momentum] is the measure of the same, coming from the velocity and quantity of matter [our mass] conjointly.

Q5 (a) Imagine two objects, A and B, such that the force on A due to B is F_A. If F_B is the force on B due to A, write an expression linking these two forces.

(*Note:* Be careful with the plus and minus signs and remember that force is a vector quantity having both magnitude and direction.)

(b) If t_B is the time for which the force F_A acts on B and t_A is the time for which force F_A acts on A, write an expression linking t_A and t_B.

(c) What is the value of the impulse on A?

(d) What is the value of the impulse on B?

(e) What can you say about the impulses on A and B when compared with each other?

(f) What can you say about the changes of momentum of A and B?

(g) What therefore must be the sum of the changes of momentum of A and B? ◆

You should have ended up with a result summarized by the law of conservation of momentum:

> In any interaction [collision or explosion] the total momentum remains unchanged.

You should make a note of this.

THE LAW OF CONSERVATION OF MOMENTUM

In any interaction [collision or explosion] the total momentum remains unchanged.

Sign convention

In all momentum investigations you will need to adopt a sign convention for the velocities of moving objects. A commonly used one is that (i) objects moving to the right are given positive velocities and (ii) objects moving to the left are given negative velocities. Momentum is a vector quantity and therefore you will have to include a sign with all values.

 An object has a mass of 10 kg. It initially has a speed of 5 m s^{-1} and after some intervention it moves at 7 m s^{-1}. The positive direction for all vectors is to the right. What is the change in momentum in the following cases?

(a) It begins and ends up moving to the left.

(b) It begins and ends up moving to the right.

(c) It begins moving to the right and ends up moving to the left.

(a) −20 kg m s^{-1} (a change from −50 kg m s^{-1} to −70 kg m s^{-1}).

(b) +20 kg m s^{-1} (a change from +50 kg m s^{-1} to +70 kg m s^{-1}).

(c) −120 kg m s^{-1} (a change from +50 kg m s^{-1} to −70 kg m s^{-1}).

The exploration and questions that follow will give you an opportunity to understand what is meant by the phrase **conservation of momentum**. Remember to use a sign convention with all vector quantities for the following questions and with the *Multimedia Motion* investigations. The law of conservation of momentum is fairly easily checked with the

Multimedia Motion sequences dealing with linear air track vehicles (Exploration 4.2) or by doing your own experiments using a linear air track (Exploration 4.3). These vehicles float on a cushion of air and move in a near frictionless environment.

Exploration 4.2   Looking at momentum with linear air track vehicles – CD ROM sequences

40-50 MINUTES

Apparatus:

◆ *Multimedia Motion* CD-ROM package
◆ IBM compatible computer running Microsoft Windows

When you finish this exploration you should have a report comprising a collection of information obtained from the computer, your calculations and your conclusions. Do not include a description of how you used the computer. Present your data clearly so that you can talk it through with other people or hand it in for marking.

Part (i)

Begin with the sequence *Air track collision 8.*

Make plots of the position of the moving vehicle before its collision with the stationary vehicle.

Continue to make plots of position after the two vehicles have stuck together.

Look at the data on the velocities before and after the collision by single clicking on the DATA button.

Obtain information on the mass of the vehicles by single clicking on the TEXT button.

Process the information obtained and write down, with calculations, how well momentum has been conserved in this collision.

Part (ii)

Write down how well the law of conservation of momentum is supported in some of the other air track collision sequences. Choose at least one in which the collision is said to be **inelastic** rather than **elastic**. (The meanings of these terms are dealt with in Section 5 on energy.)

Momentum is conserved in all collisions but, because of uncertainties in the plotting of positions and, in some cases, jumping of the vehicles, it may not always appear quite so.

Part (iii)

If you have time, look at the *Train crash* sequences.

A useful expression here is momentum = mass × velocity.

Exploration 4.3 Looking at momentum with linear air track vehicles – practical investigations

50-60
MINUTES

Apparatus:

◆ linear air track, vehicles and accessories ◆ air blower ◆ two light gates
◆ computer with interface and timing/velocity measuring software or two electronic stopclocks ◆ Blu-Tack or pin and cork

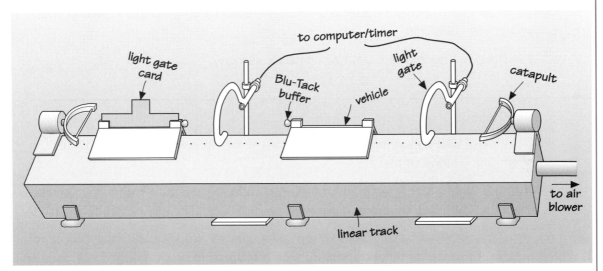

Figure 4.1 Linear air track set-up for Exploration 4.3

Part (i)

Set up the linear air track and light gates as shown, ensuring that the air track is level. To test whether it is level, place a vehicle on it and see if it drifts one way or the other.

Connect up the light gates to the computer interface or electronic stopclocks according to the equipment's instructions, loading software as appropriate.

Using two identical vehicles, fix Blu-Tack or pin and cork buffers to them. Place one vehicle at the left-hand end of the air track and the other in the middle. Set the stopclocks or software ready to take readings.

Push the vehicle at the left-hand end towards the other one and let them collide, stick together and continue to the end of the air track. Record your measurements of velocity or time. Your system may give the speed of a vehicle as it passes through a light gate. If it does not, you will need to calculate it from the measured time taken for the card to pass through the light gate:

$$\text{velocity} = \frac{\text{width of light gate card}}{\text{time through light gate}}$$

Take velocities to the right to be positive and those to the left to be negative.

Find and record the mass of each of the vehicles (complete with its buffers and timing card). Process the data obtained and write down how well momentum was conserved in the collision.

Part (ii)

Try (a) different combinations of vehicles, (b) collisions where both vehicles are initially moving and (c) collisions in which the buffers are magnetic or elastic (provide elastic collisions). Some of these arrangements will need light gate cards on each vehicle. Process the data obtained as before and again write down how well momentum was conserved in the collisions.

A useful expression here is momentum = mass × velocity.

The following questions make use of the law of conservation of momentum.

Q6 A toy balloon is blown up and then released with its mouth open. What happens and why? ◆

Q7 An astronaut in deep space takes a 'walk' outside the spacecraft in order to tighten some nuts on a navigation beacon with a spanner. The astronaut's tether to the spacecraft becomes detached. What could the astronaut do in order to get back to the spacecraft? Give your reasoning ◆

Q8 A mini-car of mass 500 kg has a head-on collision with a larger car of mass 1000 kg. The two cars stop dead. If the larger car was travelling at 20 m s^{-1} just before the collision, calculate the velocity of the mini-car just before the collision. Assume that the larger car was coming from the right. ◆

Q9 Two ice skaters moving frictionlessly on an ice-rink gently collide head-on and link arms. Just before their collision they had velocities of +0.9 m s^{-1} and −0.5 m s^{-1}.

(a) If they come to a complete stop after the collision, which skater has the greater mass?

(b) If both skaters had the same mass, what would be their velocity after the collision? ◆

Q10 A collision took place between a stationary linear air track vehicle and one moving in from the left. These then stuck together on impact and continued to move to the right. Figure 4.2 shows stroboscopic plots of position made on the initially moving vehicle after successive intervals of time of 0.1 s. The stationary vehicle was of mass 3 kg.

(a) What was the velocity of the moving vehicle before the collision?

(b) What was the velocity of the pair of vehicles after the collision?

(c) Calculate the mass of the moving vehicle. ◆

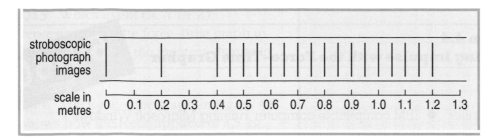

Figure 4.2
Linear air track plots

4.5 What is the system?

All the examples dealt with so far have been taken from what are known as **closed systems** – systems in which there are no resultant external forces acting. Where momentum appears not to be conserved you will need to look for other 'bodies' that are involved in the interaction. The *Train crash* sequences in *Multimedia Motion* deal with systems that are not closed.

Q11 If a piece of putty is dropped on to the floor it just stops and sticks there. However, consider the whole process from just before the putty is dropped to when it has stuck to the floor. Before it is dropped it has no momentum. Just before it sticks to the floor it had some momentum. After it stuck to the floor it has no momentum. If the law of conservation of momentum really is correct, what has been missed out? ◆

4.6 Investigating impulse

Measuring changes of momentum is fairly easy. Measuring impulses is rather more difficult because most impulses involve varying forces over time. When a golf ball is hit it does not move away from the club instantly, it deforms or squashes. Then it begins to accelerate away, and in doing so the force on it lessens until, when contact between the club and the ball is broken, no further force is exerted by the club. Force–time graphs often look like Figure 4.3.

The situation is very similar with car seatbelts. The force exerted by the belt on the driver or passenger builds up to a maximum as the belt stretches – it is not a steady force.

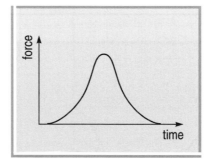

Figure 4.3
A force–time graph

You can investigate impulses through the following explorations. The SATIS 16–19 Unit 47 *Playing Safe* also has a number of activities related to this topic; they are concerned with accidents on playground surfaces.

4.7 Newton's third law of motion

There is also a third law of motion that you need to understand in order to help you make a prediction about what happens to momentum in a collision or explosion, or indeed in any interaction.

This law expresses a very simple idea: that all forces occur in pairs, equal in size, but acting in opposite directions and on different objects. We usually state it like this:

> If a body A exerts a force on body B, then body B exerts an equal and opposite force on body A.

NEWTON'S THIRD LAW OF MOTION

If a body A exerts a force on body B, then body B exerts an equal and opposite force on body A.

Q16 Consider the following situations and sketch the two objects in each case showing the two forces that act between them as suggested by Newton's third law:

(a) a person standing on the ground

(b) a satellite in orbit around the Earth

(c) a stone falling to the ground.

(*Note:* It is important always to be careful when considering pairs of forces, remembering that each acts not just in opposite directions but on different objects as well, and that each of the forces in such a pair are always of the same type.) ◆

Achievements

After working through this section you should be able to:

- apply Newton's first law of motion
- apply Newton's second law of motion in terms of force equals rate of change of momentum
- define impulse and be able to calculate the impulse of a force on an object
- determine change of momentum from a force–time graph
- use the *Force–Time Grapher* to investigate and report on impulses obtained under various conditions
- describe experiments to measure momentum, and to measure impulse
- apply Newton's third law of motion
- apply the law of conservation of linear momentum, explaining how it is a consequence of Newton's second and third laws of motion and describe experiments to verify the conservation of momentum
- use the CD-ROM package *Multimedia Motion* and/or the linear air track directly (i) to see how well the law of conservation of linear momentum is supported and (ii) to calculate the change of momentum of a kicked football, the impulse applied to it and the average force with which the ball was kicked.

Glossary

Closed system   A system within which all the objects are isolated and no resultant external forces act.

Conservation of momentum   A law or principle stating that in any interaction between objects the total momentum remains constant. Usually this appears to be true only when one is working in a closed or isolated system, but it is universally true.

Elastic collision   A collision in which the total kinetic energy of the colliding objects remains the same.

Impulse   Unit: newton second (N s). The product of the force applied and the time for which that force is applied. Impulse is a vector quantity. Its value will be equal to the change of momentum produced.

Inelastic collision   A collision in which the total kinetic energy of the colliding objects does not remain the same. Energy has been transferred elsewhere, for example in deformation, by heating things or by making sound.

Momentum   Unit: kilogram metre per second (kg m s^{-1}). The product of mass and velocity. Momentum is a vector quantity.

Answers to Ready to Study test

R1

(a)

Work done (J) = force (N) × distance (m)

$$= 50\,\text{N} \times 15\,\text{m}$$
$$= 750\,\text{J}$$
$$= 7.5 \times 10^2\,\text{J}$$

(b) Rearranging the work done expression gives

$$\text{force (N)} = \frac{\text{work done (J)}}{\text{distance (m)}}$$
$$= \frac{400\,\text{J}}{15\,\text{m}}$$
$$= 26.7\,\text{N}$$
$$= 2.7 \times 10^1\,\text{N}$$

(to two significant figures)

R2

Comments like these are usually very tongue-in-cheek and not intended to spark an intellectual debate. Occasionally, however, a serious article in a newspaper, for example, may also contain such ideas. We don't believe that energy disappears, although in another SLIPP unit on physics in space you will find out about Einstein's idea that energy and matter can interchange. Without this interchange the total amount of energy remains constant but it is constantly being transferred. We summarize this as the law of conservation of energy.

R3

(a) The distance travelled by the bus increases, though at different rates at different times, depending on its speed. This can be checked by looking at its odometer.

(b) The bus's displacement from its terminal may or may not be increasing, it may even be decreasing if the bus is on the homeward stretch.

(c) The bus's velocity will begin at zero, and then gradually increase until a steady velocity is reached. As it approaches the next stop the velocity will be gradually decreased. If there are traffic lights or any other reason for the driver to change the speed of the bus, this will result in an extra change to the velocity. Also, if the bus changes direction, for example by turning a corner, the velocity will also change as a result of this.

(d) The acceleration will be at a roughly steady value at the start of this motion and then reduce to zero as the bus reaches its steady speed. As the bus approaches the next stop the acceleration again increases to a steady value until it stops, but this time the direction is reversed. Again, if there is any additional reason for the bus to change its speed or direction between the two stops, this will be effected by a further acceleration.

R4

$$\text{force (N)} = \text{mass (kg)} \times \text{acceleration (ms}^{-2})$$
$$= 60 \text{ kg} \times 8.0 \text{ms}^{-2}$$
$$= 480 \text{ N}$$
$$= 4.8 \times 10^2 \text{ N}$$
$$\text{(to two significant figures)}$$

R5

(a) Linear momentum is the product of the mass and the velocity of an object that is not changing direction. It is a vector quantity, so we always need to state its direction. As linear means in one dimension only (or in a straight line) the direction is usually indicated by a plus or a minus sign.

$$\text{momentum} = \text{mass (kg)} \times \text{velocity (ms}^{-1})$$

(b) The units of momentum are kg m s^{-1}.

Answers to questions in the text

Q1

(a) In (1), (2) and (3) the objects were given their kinetic energy by a force acting for a short time, as they were hit. In (4) the trolley was also pushed for a short time. Therefore, in (1) to (4) the force that initiated the motion has stopped acting. The spacecraft in (5) being halfway between the Earth and Mars is almost in equilibrium, and requires no force to keep it moving. So for this situation as well, the force that began the motion is no longer acting.

(b) Friction will eventually bring the objects in situations (1), (2) and (3) to rest, unless they are caught. The trolley on the air track in (4), will finally come to rest because of air resistance (which, strictly speaking, is a type of friction, but between a fluid and a solid rather than between two solids). The spacecraft in (5), will either be brought to rest by its engines, or by making use of atmospheric (air) resistance as it approaches the surface of a planet, and friction as it hits the surface.

(c) All of the objects will continue at constant velocity until an unbalanced force acts on them. This is what Newton summarized in his first law of motion.

(d) No, the sum of all the forces acting on an object must be zero if the object is to continue in uniform motion. If the sum of the forces is not zero there will be an acceleration.

(e) The car travelling at constant velocity is just the same as any other object. Using Newton's first law we can see that for any object at constant velocity there is no resultant force.

Q2

(a) Impulse is given by

force × time of application of the force

so it is

5.0 N × 2.0 s = 10 N s

(b) Since

impulse = change of momentum

the change of momentum must be numerically the same as the impulse. So it is 10 kg m s^{-1} (as these are the units of momentum).

Q3

(a) The change of momentum is given by

mass × change of velocity

so it is

$$1000 \text{kg} \times 10 \text{ms}^{-1} = 10000 \text{kg} \text{ms}^{-1}$$
$$= 1.0 \times 10^4 \text{kg} \text{ms}^{-1}$$

(b) Again, impulse must be numerically the same as the change of momentum. So to two significant figures, it is 1.0×10^4 N s (as these are the units of impulse).

Q4

(a) The change in momentum of each dummy is given by

$(mv - mu)$

So we have

$$(75 \times 0) \text{kg} \text{ms}^{-1} - (75 \times 13.4) \text{kg} \text{ms}^{-1}$$
$$= -1005 \text{kg} \text{ms}^{-1}$$
$$= -1.0 \times 10^3 \text{kg} \text{ms}^{-1}$$
(to two significant figures)

(b) The impulse is equal to the change of momentum, so it is

$$-1005 \text{Ns} = -1.0 \times 10^3 \text{Ns}$$
(to two significant figures)

(c) Impulse $= F_{\text{average}} \times t$

so

$$-1005 \text{Ns} = F_{\text{average}} \times \left(\frac{200}{1000}\right) \text{s}$$

Giving

$$F_{\text{average}} = \frac{-1005 \text{Ns}}{0.200 \text{s}}$$
$$= -5025 \text{N}$$
$$= -5.0 \times 10^3 \text{N}$$
(to two significant figures)

(d) Impulse $= F_{\text{average}} \times t$

So

$$-1005 \text{N s} = F_{\text{average}} \times \left(\frac{2.0}{1000}\right) \text{s}$$

Giving

$$F_{average} = \frac{-1005\,\text{N}\,\text{s}}{0.0020\,\text{s}}$$

$$= -502500\,\text{N}$$

$$= -5.0 \times 10^5\,\text{N}$$

(to two significant figures)

(This is about the weight of a mini-car!)

Q5

(a) $F_A = -F_B$.

(b) $t_A = t_B$.

(c) The impulse on A is $F_A t_A$.

(d) The impulse on B is $F_B t_B$.

(e) These impulses are equal in value but opposite in direction.

(f) These changes of momentum are also equal in value but opposite in direction.

(g) Zero!

Q6

Air escapes from the mouth of the balloon at a relatively high speed and so has momentum in the direction of its escape. Before the escape of the air, neither the balloon nor the air were moving, so they had a total momentum of zero. After the escape of the air the total momentum of the escaped air and the balloon must still be zero. Therefore the balloon must move in the opposite direction to that of the escaping air in order to have a momentum equal and opposite to it.

Q7

The astronaut could throw the spanner away in a direction that is the exact opposite to that in which she or he needs to move to get back to the spacecraft. Before the spanner is thrown the astronaut's and spanner's combined momentum will be zero. After the spanner is thrown the astronaut's and spanner's combined momentum must still be zero. So, if the spanner has momentum in one direction, then the astronaut must move

in the opposite direction with an equal but opposite momentum.

Q8

Let the velocity of the mini-car be v (in m s^{-1}). The momentum of the two vehicles after the collision is 0 kg m s^{-1}, so their combined momenta before the collision must also be 0 kg m s^{-1}. The larger car has a momentum before the collision of

$$1000\ \text{kg} \times -20\ \text{m s}^{-1} = -20\,000\ \text{kg m s}^{-1}$$

(As the larger car was coming in from the right it has been given a negative velocity.)

The momentum of the mini-car before the collision is 500 kg $\times v$. Therefore

$$-20\,000\ \text{kg m s}^{-1} + 500\ \text{kg} \times v = 0$$

and so

$$v = \frac{20000\,\text{kg m s}^{-1}}{500\,\text{kg}}$$

$$= 40\,\text{m s}^{-1}$$

So the mini-car must have been travelling at 40 m s^{-1} coming from the left.

Q9

(a) The one travelling at a velocity of -0.5 m s^{-1} has the greater mass. This skater needs to have the same value of momentum, though in the opposite direction, as the skater travelling at 0.9 m s^{-1}. Since the former skater's velocity is numerically smaller, he or she must have a larger mass in order to make the momentum numerically identical.

(b) Let the mass of each skater be m (in kg). Then the momentum before the collision of the 0.9 m s^{-1} skater is $0.9m$ m s^{-1} and that of the -0.5 m s^{-1} skater is $-0.5m$ m s^{-1}. Therefore the total momentum of the pair before the collision is

$$(-0.5m + 0.9m)\,\text{m s}^{-1} = +0.4m\,\text{m s}^{-1}$$

So after the collision the total momentum of the pair must still be $+0.4m$ m s^{-1}. The pair's new momentum can now be written as $2mv$, where v is their new velocity. Therefore

$$2mv = +0.4m\,\text{ms}^{-1}$$

and so

$$v = \frac{+0.4}{2}\,\text{ms}^{-1}$$

$$= +0.2\,\text{ms}^{-1}$$

So the pair continue to move with a velocity of 0.2 m s^{-1} in the direction that the 0.9 m s^{-1} skater was originally going.

Q10

(a) Before the collision the displacement of the moving vehicle in each 0.1 s was 0.2 m, giving a velocity of 2 m s^{-1}.

(b) After the collision the displacement of the pair of vehicles in each 0.1 s was 0.05 m, giving a velocity of 0.5 m s^{-1}.

(c) Let the mass of the moving vehicle be m (in kg). Then, before the collision, the momentum of the moving vehicle was $2m$ m s^{-1} and that of the stationary vehicle 0 kg m s^{-1}, giving a total momentum of $2m$ m s^{-1}. After the collision the mass of the two vehicles stuck together was $m + 3$ kg and so their total momentum was $(m + 3\text{ kg}) \times 0.5$ m s^{-1}. Since the total momentum must remain unchanged

$$2m\,\text{ms}^{-1} = (m + 3\text{kg}) \times 0.5\,\text{ms}^{-1}$$

Expanding and rearranging terms gives

$$1.5m\,\text{ms}^{-1} = 1.5\text{kg}\,\text{ms}^{-1}$$

So

$$m = 1\text{ kg}$$

the mass of the moving vehicle is 1 kg.

Q11

The Earth will be attracting the piece of putty with a force equal to, but opposite in direction to, that with which the putty attracts the Earth. This results in the Earth moving

towards the putty as it drops. At all times during the process of dropping the Earth will have a momentum equal in value, but opposite in sign and direction, to that of the putty. The missing item was the Earth.

Q12

(a) The area under the graph represents change in momentum or impulse.

(b) At time t_1 the acceleration is at its maximum, since the force is at its maximum. Velocity and therefore momentum go on increasing as long as the force is positive.

(c) At time t_2 the body will have reached its maximum velocity and have zero acceleration.

Q13

All events gave the same change in momentum since all three have the same area under their graph plots.

Q14

(a) The impulse is given by the area under the graph, which is 20 N s.

(b) Since impulse = change of momentum it must be 20 kg m s^{-1}.

(c) Your graph, should look like Figure 4.8.

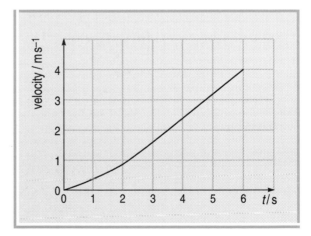

Figure 4.8 Answer for Question 14 part (c)

(d) Your graph should look like Figure 4.9.

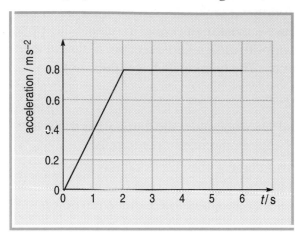

Figure 4.9 Answer for Question 14 part (d)

Talk these problems over with other students or your teacher and compare your graphs. (*Note:* Acceleration will follow the same pattern of change as force.)

Q15

(a) It is the area under the graph. In this case approximately −1.4 N s (*Note:* the axis is in milliseconds).

(b) +1.4 N s

(c) +1.4 kg m s^{-1}

(d) Using $Ft = mv - mu$ we have

$$1.4\,\text{N s} = \left(0.045\,\text{kg} \times v\right) - \left(0.045\,\text{kg} \times 0\,\text{ms}^{-1}\right)$$

So

$$v = \frac{1.4\,\text{N s}}{0.045\,\text{kg}}$$

Giving

$$v = 31.1\,\text{ms}^{-1}$$

$$= 3.1 \times 10^{1}\,\text{ms}^{-1} \text{ (to two significant figures)}$$

(e) Your graph should be the mirror image of the original above the time axis.

Q16

(a) See Figure 4.10.

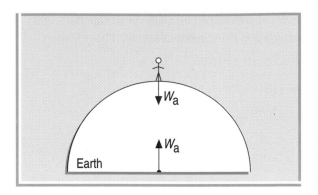

Figure 4.10 Answer for Question 16 part (a)

(b) See Figure 4.11.

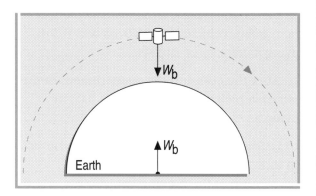

Figure 4.11 Answer for Question 16 part (b)

(c) See Figure 4.12.

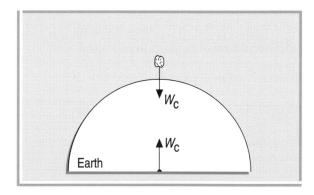

Figure 4.12 Answer for Question 16 part (c)

The forces are of the same type (weight), and act in the same directions in all three, even though these are apparently completely different situations. Only the magnitude of the force differs owing to the different masses. They are, of course, acting on the centres of gravity in each case.

In this section we will be continuing with our theme of safe transportation. In recent years vehicle manufacturers have specifically designed front and rear areas of cars so that when a car is involved in a front or rear collision with another solid object these areas will collapse in order to dissipate energy. These areas are called crumple zones as they crumple progressively so as to dissipate the energy more slowly and protect the cars' occupants. Side impact bars are also used to protect the occupants from sideways collisions. Provided they form part of the car's integrated structure, side impact bars channel impact forces to strong areas of the car, such as the roof or floorpan, and away from the occupants' cabin.

You may think that the heavier a car is the stronger it is likely to be and therefore the better able to protect you in a crash. Whilst this is true to some extent, it may not be good news for whatever you collide with! Heavy cars also use more fuel and so are more expensive to run. Some car manufacturers are now researching the use of new lightweight, but strong, materials for car bodies, such as aluminium and polymer composites. These materials will enable designers to improve fuel economy, safety and reliability. Aluminium has excellent recycling potential and research currently under way with the new polymers is looking at how their chemical recovery can create a new secondary market for scrapped vehicles. You can learn more about this in the SLIPP unit *Physics in the Environment*.

In this section you will learn about energy transfer in collisions and be investigating the relationship between cars' acceleration, power, mass and the frictional forces.

READY TO STUDY TEST

Before you begin this section you should be able to:

- describe events that show that energy has been transferred
- describe kinetic energy as the energy associated with movement
- use the terms 'work', 'energy' and 'power' correctly and give their scientific units
- distinguish between scalar and vector quantities (this was covered in Section 3)
- use the equation $F = ma$ (this was covered in Section 3)
- recall the equations of motion in a straight line with uniform acceleration, in particular $v^2 = u^2 + 2as$ (this was covered in Section 3)
- use the symbol ΔE to denote a change in energy, $\Delta E = (E_2 - E_1)$

- perform tests to show how two variables are related: whether by direct proportion or inverse proportion
- understand that momentum is conserved during collisions (this was covered in Section 4).

QUESTIONS

R1 Give the correct SI units of measurement for mass, length, time, work, energy and power.

R2 Write down the equations of motion with uniform acceleration in a straight line. Explain any symbols that you use.

5.1 Work

Throughout this unit you have seen **energy** being transferred to and from vehicles and other moving objects. Energy is transferred to vehicles to make them move and it is also transferred from vehicles in any collisions they might have. So how do you measure the energy transferred?

Your earlier science courses would have introduced you to the concept of **work**. Work gives a measure of the energy transferred by the action of a force applied over a distance. It is defined by the following expression:

work done (J) = force exerted (N)
$\qquad$ × displacement in the direction of the force (m)

or

$W = Fs$

Oddly, work done is a scalar quantity, even though it is the product of two vectors.

 How much work is done when a force of 10 N is exerted over a distance of 2.0 m?

Work done = force exerted × displacement in the direction of the force, so the work done is

10 N × 2.0 m = 20 J

Some equation work

Read through the next section very carefully. You will not be asked to reproduce this proof line by line, but you should be able to follow the derivation.

If a constant force, F, is exerted to accelerate a vehicle of mass m from an initial velocity u to a final velocity v, then its acceleration is given by

$$a = \frac{F}{m}$$

However, from one of the equations of motion we know that
$$v^2 = u^2 + 2as$$

so we can write

$$v^2 = u^2 + 2\frac{F}{m}s$$

where s is the distance over which the mass accelerates.

Multiplying both sides of the above expression by m we have
$$mv^2 = mu^2 + 2Fs$$

Now dividing both sides of the expression by 2 we have

$$\frac{1}{2}mv^2 = \frac{1}{2}mu^2 + Fs$$

or

$$Fs = \frac{1}{2}mv^2 - \frac{1}{2}mu^2$$

Since Fs is the work done on the vehicle, then $\frac{1}{2}mv^2 - \frac{1}{2}mu^2$ must be the energy transferred to it. Energy associated with movement is, as you will recall, known as **kinetic energy** (technically translational kinetic energy in this case).

$\frac{1}{2}mv^2$ is the final kinetic energy

$\frac{1}{2}mu^2$ is the initial kinetic energy

so

$\frac{1}{2}mv^2 - \frac{1}{2}mu^2$ is the *change* of kinetic energy.

Now let us see how to use these ideas and expressions.

Worked example

Calculate the change of kinetic energy of a vehicle of mass 1000 kg that accelerates from rest to a velocity of 10 m s^{-1}.

$m = 1000$ kg, $u = 0$, $v = 10$ m s^{-1}, ΔKE = ?

The change of kinetic energy, ΔKE, is given by

$$\Delta\text{KE} = \frac{1}{2}mv^2 - \frac{1}{2}mu^2$$

therefore

$$\Delta\text{KE} = \frac{1}{2}\left[1000\,\text{kg} \times \left(10\,\text{ms}^{-1}\right)^2\right] - \frac{1}{2}\left[1000\,\text{kg} \times \left(0\,\text{ms}^{-1}\right)^2\right]$$

$$= 50000\,\text{kg}\,\text{m}^2\,\text{s}^{-2}$$

$$= 50000\,\text{J}$$

so the change of kinetic energy is 5×10^4 J. ◆

 Calculate the change of kinetic energy of a vehicle of mass 1000 kg that accelerates from 10 m s^{-1} to 20 m s^{-1}.

$m = 1000$ kg, $u = 10$ m s^{-1}, $v = 20$ m s^{-1}, ΔKE = ?

$$\Delta\text{KE} = \frac{1}{2}mv^2 - \frac{1}{2}mu^2$$

$$= \frac{1}{2}\left[1000\,\text{kg} \times \left(20\,\text{ms}^{-1}\right)^2\right] - \frac{1}{2}\left[1000\,\text{kg} \times \left(10\,\text{ms}^{-1}\right)^2\right]$$

$$= 200000\,\text{J} - 50000\,\text{J}$$

$$= 150000\,\text{J}$$

so the change of kinetic energy is 1.5×10^5 J.

 A long train of goods wagons has a total mass of 800 000 kg. This is accelerated from rest to a velocity of 15 m s^{-1} by a locomotive exerting a steady pull of 100 000 N on these wagons. Calculate how great a distance is covered in reaching a velocity of 15 m s^{-1}.

$m = 800\,000$ kg, $u = 0$, $v = 15$ m s^{-1}, $F = 100\,000$ N, s = ?

$$Fs = \frac{1}{2}mv^2 - \frac{1}{2}mu^2$$

so we have

$$100000\,\text{N} \times s = \frac{1}{2}\left[800000\,\text{kg} \times \left(15\,\text{ms}^{-1}\right)^2\right] - \frac{1}{2}\left[800000\,\text{kg} \times \left(0\,\text{ms}^{-1}\right)^2\right]$$

therefore

$$s = \frac{1}{2} \times \frac{800000\,\text{kg}}{100000\,\text{N}} \times \left(15\,\text{ms}^{-1}\right)^2$$

$$= 900\,\text{m}$$

so 9.0×10^2 m is covered in reaching a velocity of 15 m s^{-1}.

In Section 4 you saw that momentum is conserved, or kept the same in total, in all types of collision. So what of energy? Whether or not energy is conserved depends on whether the collisions are **elastic** or **inelastic collisions**. Using the *Multimedia Motion* activity (Exploration 5.1), or by doing your own experiments using a linear air track (Exploration 5.2), you can analyse the movement of the vehicles, looking this time at the sum of their kinetic energies before and after collision. Energy, like work done, is not a vector quantity so you need not worry about its sign.

Exploration 5.1 Investigating kinetic energy with linear air track vehicles – CD-ROM sequences

Apparatus:

50-60 MINUTES

◆ *Multimedia Motion* CD-ROM package
◆ IBM compatible computer running Microsoft Windows

When you finish this exploration you should have a report comprising a collection of information obtained from the computer, your calculations and your conclusions. Do not include a description of how you used the computer. Present your data clearly so that you can talk it through with other people or hand it in for marking.

Part (i)

Begin with the sequence *Air track collision 8.*

Make plots of the position of the moving vehicle before its collision with the stationary vehicle.

Continue to make plots of position after the two vehicles have stuck together.

Look at the data on the velocities before and after the collision by single clicking on the DATA button.

Obtain information on the mass of the vehicles by single clicking on the TEXT button.

Process the information obtained. Write down, with calculations, what happened to the total kinetic energy of the vehicles before and after the collision.

Part (ii)

Write down how the total kinetic energy of the vehicles before and after collisions is affected by whether those collisions are elastic or inelastic.

A useful expression here is $\text{kinetic energy} = \frac{1}{2}mv^2$.

Exploration 5.2 Investigating kinetic energy with linear air track vehicles – practical investigations

100-120
MINUTES

Apparatus:

◆ linear air track, vehicles and accessories   ◆ air blower
◆ two light gates   ◆ light gate card   ◆ Blu-Tack or pin and cork
◆ computer with interface and timing/velocity measuring software or two electronic stopclocks

Part (i)

Set up the linear air track and light gates as shown in Figure 5.1, ensuring that the air track is level. To test whether it is level, place a vehicle on it and see if it drifts one way or the other.

Connect up the light gates to the computer interface or electronic stopclocks according to the equipment's instructions, loading software as appropriate.

Using two identical vehicles, fix Blu-Tack or pin and cork buffers to them. Place one vehicle at the left-hand end of the air track and the other in the middle. Set the stopclocks or software ready to take readings.

Push the vehicle at the left-hand end towards the other one and let them collide, stick together and continue to the end of the air track. Record your measurements of velocity or time. Your system may give the speed of a vehicle as it passes through a light gate. If it does not, you will need to calculate it from the measured time taken for the card to pass through the light gate:

$$\text{velocity} = \frac{\text{width of light gate card}}{\text{time through light gate}}$$

Find and record the mass of each of the vehicles (complete with its buffers and timing card). Process the data obtained and write down what happened to the total kinetic energy of the vehicles before and after the collision. This collision would be inelastic.

Part (ii)

Try (a) different combinations of vehicles, (b) collisions where both vehicles are initially moving and (iii) collisions in which the buffers are magnetic or elastic (provide elastic collisions). Some arrangements will need light gate cards on each vehicle. Process the data obtained as before and again report on what happened to the total kinetic energy of the vehicles before and after the collisions.

A useful expression here is $\text{kinetic energy} = \frac{1}{2}mv^2$.

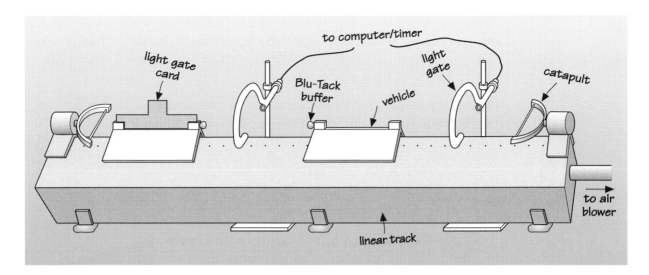

Figure 5.1 Linear air track set-up for Exploration 5.2

If you tried Explorations 5.1 or 5.2 you should have found that the total kinetic energy remained the same *only* in the collisions said to be elastic. Some of the kinetic energy had been transferred elsewhere in those collisions said to be inelastic, i.e. collisions in which deformation or squashing took place as the vehicles collided.

(*Note:* Even with elastic collisions you may have found that kinetic energy was not quite conserved. This is due to uncertainties in the plotting of positions, a little air resistance and, in some cases, jumping of the vehicles on the track. The last of these causes direct contact with the track resulting in energy transfer to it. In other words the collision was not truly elastic.)

 Would you expect a car crash to be an elastic or an inelastic collision? Explain your choice.

Inelastic. A lot of deformation (crushing and bending) takes place, also a lot of noise results from energy that has been transferred to the movement of air molecules to produce sound.

5.2 Work and power

Car engines do a lot of work, some far more quickly than others. Those working the most quickly are said to be more powerful and they transfer energy at a faster rate. The term **power** is defined as the rate at which work is done, so

$$\text{average power} \left(\text{J s}^{-1} \text{or W} \right) = \frac{\text{work done (J)}}{\text{time taken (s)}}$$

How might the maximum velocity of a car be related to its maximum power output? Would you expect the fastest cars to be those that develop the greatest power output? These two questions, along with others, can be looked at in Exploration 5.3.

(*Note:* If you don't have the data file and a computer you can do the exploration using a printout of the car data spreadsheet given in Appendix 5.1 at the end of this section.)

 Exploration 5.3   Car data analysis

50-60 MINUTES

Apparatus:
◆ Spreadsheet data file *Car data*
◆ Spreadsheet software: Lotus 123, Works, Excel, etc.
◆ IBM compatible computer

In this exploration you will be asked to look at the relationships between pairs of variables. Remember that it is possible to explore relationships by graphical or algebraic methods. Both methods are valid.

(*Note:* Remember that when you plot two variables on a graph and get a straight line it is not proof of a directly proportional relationship unless that line goes through the origin.)

Part (i)

Using data from ten cars, see to what extent their powers are proportional to their maximum speeds. Ensure that your selections are well spread across the power range. Comment on your findings.

Part (ii)

Using data from ten cars, see if there is a relationship between their powers and the time taken to accelerate from 0 to 60 mph. Ensure that your selections are well spread across the power range. Comment on your findings.

Part (iii)

There are a number of other relationships between data that could be examined. Select and investigate some of these, again reporting on your findings.

Q1 (a) What can you say about the maximum frictional force F_{fmax} and the maximum engine thrust F_{emax} when a car is travelling at its maximum velocity?

(b) How much work will the engine do against the frictional force over a displacement s when the car is at its maximum velocity?

(c) If this work is done in a time t, what is the maximum power developed by the engine?

(d) Write an expression for the maximum velocity v_{max} in terms of s and t.

(e) Using your answers to (c) and (d) write an expression for the maximum power developed by the engine in terms of the maximum frictional force F_{fmax} and the maximum velocity v_{max} of the car.

(f) The Ford Granada 2.0i Ghia is quoted by a car magazine as having a maximum velocity of 50 m s^{-1} (112 mph) and a maximum power output of 89.5 kW (120 hp). Calculate the frictional force on this car when it is travelling at its maximum velocity. ◆

Achievements

After working through this section you should be able to:

- define energy, work and power, and give their correct units of measurement
- relate work done to transfer of energy
- derive and use the formula $\frac{1}{2}mv^2$ for kinetic energy
- state and use the fact that kinetic energy is conserved only during an elastic collision
- derive and apply the expression relating the maximum power developed by a vehicle to the maximum frictional force on it and its maximum velocity
- test for mathematical relationships between independent variables
- use computer-held data.

Glossary

Elastic collision   A collision in which the total kinetic energy of the colliding objects remains the same.

Energy   Unit: joule (J). The measure of the capacity of a body or system to do work. Energy is scalar quantity.

Inelastic collision   A collision in which the total kinetic energy of the colliding objects does not remain the same. Energy has been transferred elsewhere, for example in deformation, by heating things or by making sound.

Kinetic energy   Unit: joule (J). The energy associated with movement. It is calculated from $\frac{1}{2} \times \text{mass} \times (\text{speed})^2$. Energy is a scalar quantity.

Power   Unit: watt (W). The rate at which work is done or energy is transferred. It can be expressed in terms of newton

metres per second (N m s^{-1}) or joules per second (J s^{-1}) as well as watts (W). Work is a scalar quantity.

Work   Unit: joule (J). A measure of energy transferred by the action of a force applied over a distance. Movement is always involved, even if it is only a change of shape. It can be expressed in terms of newton metres (N m) as well as joules (J). Work is a scalar quantity.

Answers to Ready to Study test

R1

Mass: kilogram (kg); length: metre (m); time: second (s); work: joule (J); energy: joule (J); power: watt (W).

R2

The equations for motion are:

$v = u + at$

$s = ut + \frac{1}{2}at^2$

$v^2 = u^2 + 2as$

and the less used

$s = vt - \frac{1}{2}at^2$

where u is the initial velocity in m s^{-1}, v is the final velocity in m s^{-1}, a is the acceleration in m s^{-2}, t is the time taken in seconds and s is the displacement in metres.

Answers to questions in the text

Q1

(a) The two forces are equal in value but opposite in direction. There is then a balanced force acting and so no further acceleration takes place.

(b) Work done = force exerted $\times$ displacement in the direction of the force

so we have

$W = F_{\text{fmax}} \times s$

(c)

$$\text{Maximum power} = \frac{\text{work done}}{\text{time taken}}$$

$$= \frac{F_{\text{f max}} \times s}{t}$$

(d)

$$v_{\text{max}} = \frac{s}{t}$$

(e)

$$\text{Maximum power} = \frac{\text{work done}}{\text{time taken}}$$

$$= \frac{F_{\text{f max}} \times s}{t}$$

$$= F_{\text{f max}} \times v_{\text{max}}$$

so

maximum power = maximum frictional force
$\times$ maximum velocity

(f)

Maximum power = maximum frictional force
$\times$ maximum velocity

so we have

89.5×10^3 W = maximum frictional force
$\times 50$ m s^{-1}

so

maximum frictional force

$$= \frac{89.5 \times 10^3 \text{ W}}{50 \text{m s}^{-1}}$$

$$= 1790 \text{ N}$$

$$= 1.8 \times 10^3 \text{ N or } 1.8 \text{ k N}$$

(to two significant figures)

Appendix 5.1

Make	Model	Fuel consumption/mpg			Mass/kg	Cylinder capacity/cc	Maximum speed/mph	Time/s 0–60 mph	Power/h
		Urban	56mph	75mph					
BMW	530i V8	19.3	35.3	28.8	1565	2997	142	7.3	218
CITROEN	AX Echo Plus 5dr	39.8	60.1	42.8	1150	1124	96	12.9	60
CITROEN	ZX1.9 Advantage Diesel	42.2	64.2	47.9	1024	1905	98	14.2	71
FIAT	Pino 55 S1.1 5dr	35.8	60.1	43.5	865	1108	93	16.5	55
FIAT	Tipo 1.4ie S 5dr	31.7	52.3	38.7	1030	1372	98	14.8	71
FORD	Fiesta 1.6 Ghia 5dr	30.4	45.6	36.3	980	1597	109	11.2	90
FORD	Escort 1.6i Ghia 5dr	31.0	49.6	40.9	1140	1597	108	11.5	90
FORD	Mondeo 1.6 5dr	28.0	51.4	39.8	1235	1598	113	12.9	90
FORD	Granada Ghia 24V 4dr	18.7	33.6	28.0	1433	2933	140	8.2	195
HONDA	Civic 1.5LSi 3dr	32.1	35.4	39.2	980	1493	108	10.5	90
HONDA	Accord 2.0i LS	25.4	40.9	34.0	1300	1997	122	9.2	131
JAGUAR	XJ6 3.2 Sport	19.3	35.3	29.7	1800	3239	138	7.9	219
LADA	Riva 1500 E	29.4	39.8	28.8	995	1452	93	14.0	66
LADA	Samara 1500 GL 5dr	29.7	48.7	36.2	915	1499	97	14.0	75
LEXUS	GS300	20.2	36.2	29.7	1700	2997	136	9.5	209
LOTUS	Esprit 34	17.9	36.2	29.9	1336	2174	165	4.7	264
LOTUS	Esprit Sport	18.8	34.5	27.4	1306	2174	168	4.4	300
MERCEDES-BENZ	E 320	20.2	31.7	26.2	1490	3199	144	7.8	220
NISSAN	Micra 1.0L 3dr	47.1	58.8	42.2	775	998	89	15.2	54
NISSAN	Sunny 1.6 SR 3dr	34.0	53.3	40.4	1025	1597	113	10.2	102
NISSAN	ZX 3.0 Twin Turbo	18.0	34.0	27.4	1615	2960	155	5.6	263
PEUGEOT	306 1.4 XN 5dr	34.0	56.5	41.5	1020	1360	100	12.9	75
PEUGEOT	405 Style 1.6i	28.8	48.7	36.7	1060	1580	114	11.1	90
PORSCHE	968 Coupe 6-sp	19.1	39.3	32.1	1370	2990	153	6.1	240
PROTON	1.3 GE	34.1	44.8	38.2	950	1299	96	13.9	74
PROTON	Personna 1.5 GLSi 4dr	32.7	50.5	38.2	970	1468	108	12.1	89
RENAULT	Clio 1.2 RN 5dr	38.5	60.2	44.6	835	1171	96	14.7	60
ROVER	Mini Sprite	37.3	54.2	33.8	685	1275	87	13.4	50
ROVER	Mini Cooper 1.3i	36.6	48.9	33.6	696	1275	92	11.5	63
ROVER	Metro 1.1 Quest 5dr	40.9	58.9	43.6	838	1120	96	14.4	60
ROVER	Maestro 1.3 Clubman 4sp	32.5	45.0	33.2	945	1275	96	13.6	66
ROVER	220 Turbo Coupe	25.4	45.8	35.9	1133	1994	150	6.6	200
SAAB	9000S 2.0i 5dr	25.0	42.8	36.7	1290	1985	122	9.5	133
SAAB	9000CD 2.0 Ecopower 4dr	23.5	40.4	32.8	1345	1985	131	9.5	155
SEAT	Marbella 900 Fun	35.3	55.4	41.5	680	903	84	19.0	41
SEAT	Ibiza 1.4S 5dr	30.7	54.3	40.4	920	1391	97	13.9	60
SEAT	Toledo 2.0 GT	26.6	45.6	36.7	1225	1984	134	8.4	150
SKODA	Favorit GLXi	35.8	49.6	35.8	930	1289	85	13.6	54
TOYOTA	Starlet 1.3GLi 4dr	37.7	53.3	39.8	840	1296	106	10.6	74
TOYOTA	Corolla 1.3GLi 4dr	36.7	53.5	40.4	1080	1332	104	12.7	87
TOYOTA	Carina E GLi 2.0 4dr	29.4	47.9	37.7	1225	1998	124	8.8	131
VAUXHALL	Corsa 1.2i Merit 3dr	36.7	52.3	39.8	835	1195	90	18.0	45
VAUXHALL	Astra 1.6i GLS 4dr	33.6	53.3	40.4	1064	1598	113	10.5	100
VAUXHALL	Cavalier 1.6i LS 4dr	31.7	54.3	41.5	1110	1598	102	14.1	75
VAUXHALL	Calibra V6	24.8	42.8	34.4	1340	2498	143	8.2	170
VOLKSWAGEN	Polo GL 1.6 5dr	32.8	53.3	39.2	990	1598	107	12.5	75
VOLKSWAGEN	Golf GTi 5dr	27.4	48.7	38.2	1140	1984	119	9.5	115
VOLVO	440 Li	26.2	50.4	39.2	1015	1794	109	11.4	89
VOLVO	GLT 2.0	23.2	42.8	33.6	1469	1984	119	11.7	143

From your work on the earlier sections of this unit you will have seen how the design of vehicles and the addition of devices such as seatbelts and airbags can reduce injury in a crash. Fortunately there are relatively few crashes, considering the enormous number of cars, motorcycles, bicycles, buses, coaches, lorries, trains, boats and aircraft that carry the world's population. The two main reasons for this are that vehicles can be steered and braked. We will now look at braking systems and the physics involved in their operation.

The major physical principle behind braking is the force we call friction. It is also possible to use electromagnetic induction – this will feature in Section 8.

All braking and steering depends on a vehicle's only connection with the road, namely tyres. Various articles on tyres have appeared in recent *Which?* reports. See if your teacher or library has copies for you to read.

In the mid 1990s both Michelin and Pirelli produced an 'energy tyre' which they claimed reduced fuel consumption by up to 5%. You may be interested to find out how this was achieved.

READY TO STUDY TEST

Before you begin this section you should be able to:

- discuss the nature of friction as a force that opposes motion
- describe the properties of materials using terms such as 'elastic', 'stiff', 'plastic', 'ductile', 'malleable', 'strong', 'tough' and 'brittle'
- use the relationships

  $F = ma$

  work done $= Fs$

  kinetic energy $= \frac{1}{2}mv^2$

  transfer of energy = work done by a force
- describe the transfer of thermal energy by conduction, convection and radiation
- relate a rise in temperature to a gain in thermal energy
- estimate uncertainties in experimental data: your own and other people's
- use techniques that allow the detection of movement and eventual calculation of speeds of movement, including rotation.

QUESTIONS

R1 Choose from the terms 'stiff', 'strong', 'tough' and 'brittle' to describe the physical properties of the following materials:
(a) biscuit; (b) steel; (c) nylon.

STOP! DON'T MOVE!

R2 If the friction between your feet and the ground is large enough you can resist being pulled along.

(a) If your friends are pulling you to the right, in which direction does the frictional force act on your shoes?

(b) Several friends pull at once and you find yourself moving to the right. In which direction does the frictional force act now?

R3 Which of the following make use of friction?

(a) The brake block of a bike.

(b) Slowing down a lunar module in space.

(c) A knot in a rope.

R4 Which property is true for all forces?

(a) A force makes objects accelerate.

(b) A force will change the shape of objects.

(c) A force can cause a change in the motion of moving objects.

R5 Students made these estimates of the sizes of the following three forces: (a) the weight of a large man, (b) the tension in a fishing line pulling in a trout of about 1.5 kg (3 lb), (c) the weight of a postage stamp.

Which student do you think gave the best estimates?

Student A: (a) 1000 N, (b) 15 N, (c) 0.000 1 N

Student B: (a) 1000 N, (b) 5 N, (c) 0.1 N

Student C: (a) 100 N, (b) 150 N, (c) 10 N

Student D: (a) 10 000 N, (b) 150 N, (c) 10 N.

R6 (a) Decide which words fit in the spaces so that the passage is scientifically correct.

Energy is _____ when there is a temperature difference between two objects. The process is more likely to be by conduction when the two objects are _____, and by when the two objects are liquid and gas.

(b) In what way is radiation a significantly different process from conduction and convection?

R7 Gyda claimed that she lived a distance of 6.430 km from college with an uncertainty of ±0.002 km.

(a) What is the least distance to her home and what is the greatest likely distance?

(b) Do you think that she could measure to this degree of accuracy?

6.1 The friction brake

The most common form of braking used on motor vehicles is based on **friction**. Any increase in the frictional force will result in greater braking of the vehicle and so slow it down, or stop it, more quickly. Most cars and motorcycles are fitted with disc brakes. Each disc of steel is connected to the axle of a wheel and is pushed against by the brake pads. The harder the pads push against the disc, the greater the frictional force.

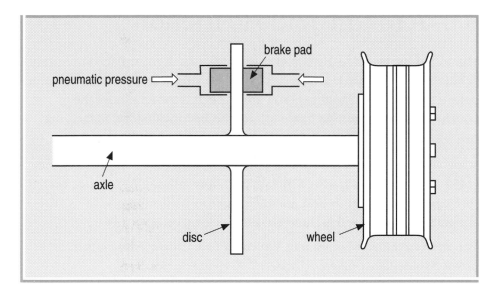

Figure 6.1
How a disk brake works

While braking, the kinetic energy of the vehicle will be transferred to the disc and brake pads making them hot. However, by constructing the disc of metal and letting it spin in air, the disc can be kept relatively cool. Where very large energy transfers are involved, cooling and ventilation of the brake disc is employed.

 What do you think are the advantages of making the brake disc out of a metal such as steel?

Steel is a cheap material and so keeps the product at a competitive price. It is **strong** and so can withstand large forces before breaking. It is **stiff** and so will not bend easily. It is **tough** and so will not crack readily. It is **ductile** and so can be moulded or pressed into shape easily.

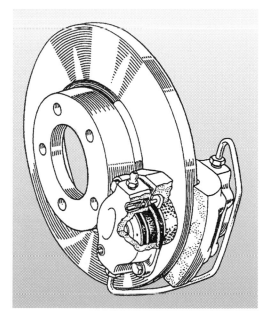

Figure 6.2
A disc brake

Q1 How does allowing the brake disc to spin in the air help to transfer the energy away from it? Use the terms **conduction** and **convection** in your answer. ◆

Some transfers of energy take place because of **radiation**; this is noticeable on racing cars where it is sometimes possible to see the brakes glowing red.

Q2 The brake discs of some racing cars are made of carbon fibre. Carbon fibre is not as good a **thermal conductor** as steel, so what property or properties might it have that makes it suited to the brakes of racing cars? ◆

6.2 A rough guide to friction

The following passage gives you some of the background to our current beliefs about friction. Use your textbooks to supplement this information before tackling the questions. You are expected to remember the conclusions that scientists come to, not the historical story. Make your own notes for future reference.

Have you ever wondered how friction comes about? Leonardo da Vinci (1452–1529) made a study of friction and how solid objects move on flat surfaces. He went on to describe their motion with rules and laws. The apparatus that he used is shown in the drawing on page 97.

You may have used equipment similar to Leonardo's apparatus in previous science courses.

One of the early attempts at an explanation for friction came from Guillaume Amontons (1663–1705) – a French physicist. He in fact rediscovered and stated the first of the three laws given below:

- The frictional force is independent of the surface area in contact provided that the force between the surfaces, and the nature of those surfaces, remain the same.
- The frictional force is proportional to the force pressing the two surfaces together.
- The frictional force is independent of the relative speed of movement between the two surfaces.

Amontons had the idea that even smooth-looking surfaces were really rough if you could look closely enough, rather like those shown in Figure 6.3.

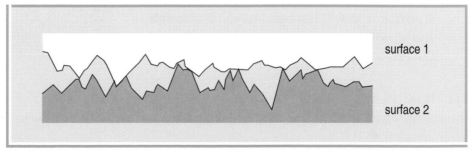

Figure 6.3 Even smooth surfaces are rough when you look closely

LEONARDO DA VINCI

The term Renaissance man was coined to describe the genius of Leonardo da Vinci. He was a man of so many accomplishments in so many areas that his like has rarely been seen in human history. You may know him as the painter of *La Gioconda*, more commonly called *The Mona Lisa*, and of *The Last Supper*, painted on the wall of the dining hall in the monastery of Santa Maria delle Grazie in Milan, Italy.

These paintings alone would have assured him enduring fame as an artist, but they should not obscure the fact that he was also a sculptor, an architect and a man of science who did serious investigations into the natural and physical sciences, mathematics, mechanics and engineering.

More than 300 years before flying machines were perfected, Leonardo devised plans for prototypes of an aeroplane and a helicopter. He was also frequently consulted by workmen in the fields of architecture, fortifications, and weaponry, and he served as a hydraulic and mechanical engineer.

Leonardo always gave precedence to illustration over the written word and he recorded his ideas and inventions in a large number of notebooks, many of which have survived. His drawings, therefore, do not illustrate the text, but the text serves to explain the pictures. In these notebooks he envisaged treating four major themes: a treatise on the science of painting, a treatise on architecture, a book on the elements of mechanics, and a general work on human anatomy. To these themes were eventually added notes on his studies of botany, geology, aerology and hydrology. Leonardo's intent was to synthesize all of his investigations with a unified world view based on his perceptions. He believed that true knowledge derived from what he called 'knowing how to see', not from philosophical speculations.

(Source: *Comptons Encyclopaedia*.)

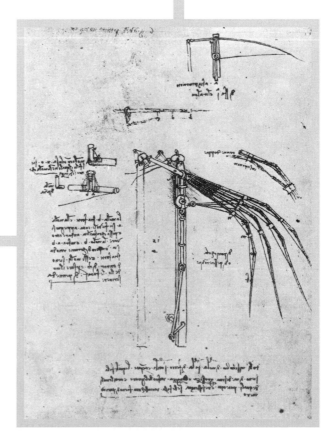

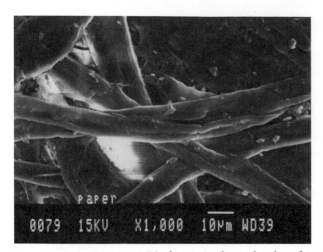

Scanning electron microscope picture of a smooth paper surface

As the top surface in Figure 6.3 moves, the humps and bumps have to slide up and over those in the bottom surface. The heavier the upper block, the more force would be needed to move it up and over the bumps. However, there was a problem. Would it not then be easier to move as it slid down the other side of the bumps? Even if there were millions of humps and bumps, there would still be no overall rising or falling and hence no force would be needed to keep the block moving. Quite a problem!

Today it is thought that friction has far more to do with the attraction of molecules for each other when they are extremely close. Even on a smooth surface there will be humps and bumps and so some molecules in each surface will be in closer contact than others.

As the surfaces are moved, these points of contact are broken, remade elsewhere and again broken. The overall force needed to move the surfaces will probably depend on the area of the points in contact. The larger the load, the more points of contact, and hence strong molecular attractions, there are likely to be. Then a greater force will be needed to move the surfaces relative to each other.

When there is continued frictional contact a rise in temperature usually results, because of the energy transfer taking place. This heating often softens the materials enough to bring about a greater area of contact, and yet increased friction rarely results. Why might that be? It is thought that this temperature increase has brought about a change in the molecular forces holding the materials together. If melting takes place then the surfaces could have a liquid layer between them. Molecules in the liquid state can easily slide past each other, and so little friction results. When this happens with friction brakes it is called **fading**. It is thought to occur when the resin bonding the materials within the brake pads oozes to the surface. Needless to say, any liquid between the surfaces also lessens the likelihood of strong molecular contact between the surfaces because it keeps them apart.

Q3 The static frictional force (the force required to just move a stationary object) is usually greater than the sliding or dynamic frictional force (the force required to move objects relative to each other once they have got going). Explain why you think this might be. ◆

Until recently, brake pads on modern cars were usually made of an asbestos filler with chopped up pieces of wire, bonded together with a resin. As asbestos dust is known to increase the risk of lung cancer, some substitutes for asbestos are also now in use. The synthetic fibre Kevlar is used by at least one company and others are using combinations of steel and mineral fibres. The pads are mounted on cast-iron bases.

Q4 What are the main advantages of mounting the brake pads on cast-iron? ◆

Q5 Why do you think brake pads have chopped up bits of wire bonded into them? ◆

Q6 Racing cars use tyres without treads (known as slicks) on hot dry days, but on cold wet days they need tyres with a tread. Why do you think this is? (*Note:* It is illegal to use slicks on public roads.) ◆

At this stage you may find it helpful and interesting to investigate the effect of frictional braking on the stopping of a vehicle. Consult your teacher about any practical work in order to arrange space and time to use a laboratory. Brief notes on how you might begin such a task are provided in Exploration 6.1 and fuller details are available from your teacher if required.

But first you will need some theory to go with your exploration. This is provided in Section 6.3 below. Study this section and its worked example. The methods are similar to those you used when you developed the formula for kinetic energy. You will then have an opportunity to see if you can apply the method for yourself.

6.3 Some mathematics to consider

Earlier you will have learnt that the kinetic energy of an object is given by

$$\frac{1}{2}mv^2$$

so, in going from a speed u to a speed v, an object of mass m will have energy transferred to it of

$$\frac{1}{2}mv^2 - \frac{1}{2}mu^2$$

In a braking situation this energy transfer will have been brought about by a braking force F acting over a braking distance s. The work done by this braking force is given by Fs, assuming that this braking force remains constant. In a real situation the driver is likely to change the braking force, but your investigation is best tackled with a near constant braking force. As you will recall from Section 5, the work done by the forces acting on a body is equal to the change of kinetic energy produced. Therefore we can write

$$Fs = \frac{1}{2}mv^2 - \frac{1}{2}mu^2$$

If the body (in the suggested investigation this is a dynamics trolley) is brought to a stop then $v = 0$, and so we have

$$Fs = -\frac{1}{2}mu^2$$

The minus sign shows that the body's kinetic energy has been reduced rather than increased, as energy is not a vector. Rearranging gives

$$s = -\frac{mu^2}{2F}$$

Q7   What does the expression above suggest about the relationship between the braking distance and (a) the trolley's mass, (b) the braking force, (c) the trolley's initial speed? ◆

Let's look at a worked example of some calculations involving these braking variables.

Worked example

If a car of mass 1000 kg was braked from 30 m s^{-1} to a stop in 60 m, what was the average braking force applied? What would initially happen to the brake disc and pads as a result of this energy transfer?

The work done by the average braking force, F, measured in newtons, will be given by

$(F \times 60)$ J

The transfer of kinetic energy brought about by this braking will have been

$$\frac{1}{2}\left[1000\,\text{kg} \times \left(0\,\text{m s}^{-1}\right)^2\right] - \frac{1}{2}\left[1000\,\text{kg} \times \left(30\,\text{m s}^{-1}\right)^2\right] = -450\,000\,\text{J}$$

(*Note:* The minus sign shows that the energy has been reduced.)

So

$(F \times 60)$ J = 450 000 J

and

$$F = \frac{450\,000\,\text{J}}{60\,\text{m}}$$

$$= 7500\,\text{N}$$

So the average braking force was 7500 N.

The initial result of this energy transfer to the brake disc and pads will be a rise in their temperatures. ◆

If you have seen the police measuring up after a traffic accident, you might have suspected that the speed of a vehicle just prior to skidding can be estimated from the length of the skid marks.

You can use the same relationship between work done by the frictional braking force between the road surface and the tyres, and the kinetic energy transferred from the vehicle. However, to find the value of the frictional braking force we need to know a quantity μ (lowercase Greek

letter mu) called the **coefficient of friction** (more fully, the coefficient of sliding or dynamic friction). One of the laws of friction that Da Vinci and Amontons discovered indicates that

$$F \propto N$$

or

$$\frac{F}{N} = \text{constant}$$

It is this constant that is called the coefficient of sliding or dynamic friction and is given the symbol μ. With both F and N being forces, μ has no units of its own.

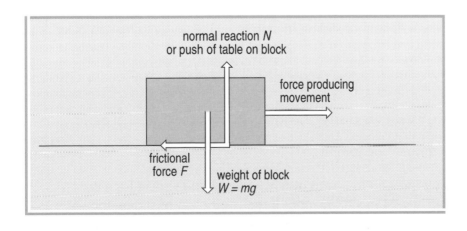

Figure 6.4
Forces acting on a block

On a flat surface the normal reaction, N, is equal in value to the weight, mg, of the object. So we now have

$$\frac{F}{mg} = \mu$$

or

$$F = \mu mg$$

On a dry road the coefficient of sliding friction, regardless of the weight of the vehicle or its tyres' condition, can vary between around 0.4 and greater than 1. So, if F is the frictional braking force between the road and the tyres, s the skid-to-a-stop distance, m the vehicle's mass, μ the coefficient of sliding friction, u the speed of the vehicle just prior to skidding and g the gravitational field strength, then:

$$\text{work done against friction} = Fs$$
$$= \mu mgs$$
$$\text{kinetic energy transferred} = \frac{1}{2}mu^2$$

So

$$\mu mgs = \frac{1}{2}mu^2$$

and

$$u = \sqrt{2\mu gs}$$

or

$$s = \frac{u^2}{2\mu g}$$

Q8   Is the estimated speed just before the skid takes place likely to be higher than, lower than or the same as the speed at which the driver began to brake? Explain. ◆

Let us now estimate how fast a car was going just before skidding 40 m. Take the coefficient of sliding friction to be 0.8 and g to be 9.81 N kg^{-1}.

$$u = \sqrt{2\mu gs}$$

so

$$u = \sqrt{2 \times 0.8 \times 9.81\,\text{N kg}^{-1} \times 40\,\text{m}}$$

$$\cong 25\,\text{m s}^{-1} \text{ or } 56\,\text{mph}$$

Q9   (a) What skid-to-a-stop distance would you expect for a car travelling at 13.4 m s^{-1} (30 mph) if the coefficient of sliding friction was 0.8 and $g = 9.81$ N kg^{-1}? (b) If, on a wet day, this coefficient of sliding friction is reduced to 0.4, calculate how long the skid-to-a-stop distance will be at this same speed. ◆

Exploration 6.1   To investigate friction braking

50-60 MINUTES

Apparatus:

◆ equipment as shown in Figure 6.5

> Anyone cutting ceramic mats or brake pads should wear a dust mask to prevent inhalation of dust and use a damp cloth to clear up.

The most important factor in braking is the *stopping distance*, so this will be your dependent variable. There are many independent variables, which could include:

■ vehicle mass

■ braking force

■ vehicle's initial speed or kinetic energy.

First you should write down how, in the light of your knowledge, you think the stopping distance might be related to each of the independent variables. Then proceed to investigate, collect, record and analyse the resulting data and finally compare your conclusions with your predictions providing, where necessary and possible, explanations for their not agreeing. Figure 6.5 shows a possible arrangement of the equipment.

If you have a range of materials available then you might like to extend or change the nature of the investigation and answer the question 'What is the best combination of materials to have for the brake band and pad?' The manufacturers of brake pads have certainly looked into this.

Hints and tips

A suitable material for the brake band is the steel strip sometimes used for wrapping heavy parcels. An alternative is kitchen aluminium foil, although this may well need folding lengthways a number of times to make it strong enough. The brake pad material could be from a real brake pad, as long as this does not contain any asbestos. A good substitute is the ceramic mat material used to stand Bunsen burners on.

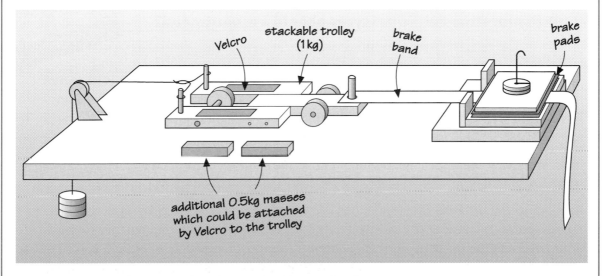

Figure 6.5 Possible set-up of equipment for Exploration 6.1

Arrange for a known force to just be able to pull your trolley along at constant velocity. A convenient method is to hang weights (masses) on a string over a pulley and connect it to the trolley. Give the trolley a small push to get it moving. Judgement of constant velocity (zero acceleration) could be made by eye, but you will be much more accurate if you use a light gate or ticker timer.

The weight, W, of your masses, m, will be given by the expression $W = mg$, where g is the gravitational field strength of approximately 9.81 N kg^{-1}.

Answer the following questions in your account of this exploration.

 Why is it necessary to get the trolley to move at constant velocity?

It is only then you know that you have balanced forces.

Q10 What is the relationship between the weight of the masses hung on the end of the string and the frictional force being applied? ◆

The trolley's mass should include the mass of the brake band. Energy can be transferred to the trolley very easily by catapulting it with an elastic band stretched across the runway. When doing this do, of course, remove the string and hanging weight.

The trolley's initial speed or kinetic energy is best determined from measurements made with a light gate. Care will be needed to ensure that enough slack is put into the brake band to allow the initial speed to be attained and measured prior to the brakes being applied.

Fuller details of this area of study can be found in *The Physics of Traffic Accident Investigation* (Tao, 1987).

 Exploration 6.2   What tyres should I recommend?

50-60
MINUTES

Resources:

◆ *Which?* reports ◆ magazine articles ◆ manufacturers' information and relevant books ◆ overhead projector ◆ flipchart or presentation graphics software (e.g. Freelance Graphics, Harvard Graphics or similar) ◆ computer

Imagine that you are responsible for the maintenance of your company's fleet of hire cars. With new designs of tyres coming on to the market, some of which claim to save up to 5% in fuel, you wish to fit those best suited to as many cars as possible.

In order to get your recommendations taken further you need to give a presentation to the directors, backed up by relevant data and, where possible, explanatory detail. In your presentation (to your student colleagues and teaching staff) you could use (i) an overhead projector, (ii) computer presentation graphics, (iii) flipcharts, or a combination of these and other media.

6.4 Anti-lock braking

Having a braking system on a vehicle does not automatically ensure safe braking. Controlled braking without the brakes locking is what is required.

Research has shown that some 10% of accidents involving vehicles without anti-lock brakes were due to the locking of the brakes. The first use of such a system was back in 1947 on a Boeing B-47 bomber and then more generally on aircraft from the 1950s onward with the Dunlop Maxaret system.

So why is the braking of a vehicle not achieved in the shortest possible distance, and under control, with ordinary brakes? Mainly because so few drivers can judge when to ease pressure on the brake pedal in order to prevent a skid in which directional and speed control is lost.

One of the problems is the change of **adhesion** between the road surface and the tyres, this changes with the condition and type of both road and tyre surfaces and the percentage of **wheel slip** (0% wheel slip is no slip at all, 100% wheel slip is a totally locked wheel).

 Why is some wheel slip necessary?

If there was no wheel slip at all, the tyre would merely be rolling on the road, not being braked by its surface at all. Hence some wheel slip is needed if any braking or grip is required.

 Look at the graph shown in Figure 6.6. (a) What percentage of wheel slip gives the largest adhesive force **longitudinally**? (b) In which direction does this longitudinal adhesion control the slip?

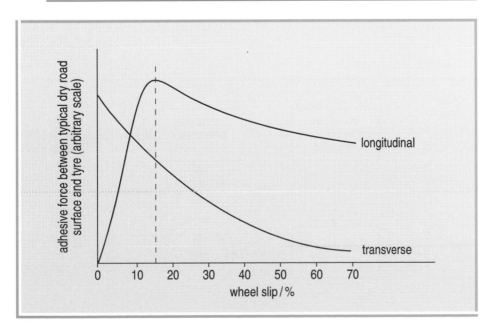

Figure 6.6
Adhesive force versus wheel slip

(a) Approximately 15% wheel slip provides the largest adhesive force longitudinally. (b) In the forward direction of rotation of the wheel and car.

 What is unfortunate about the relationship between **transverse** adhesion and percentage wheel slip?

The adhesive force reduces immediately any slip takes place.

 How do you think the graphs would change if the road surface was covered with ice? Draw a new set of curves to compare with those in Figure 6.6.

Your curves should be similarly shaped lines, but each lower than the corresponding curves in Figure 6.6.

How might you go about detecting the amount of slippage of the wheels? It requires the measurement of the difference between the wheel speed at the wheel and that inferred from the measurement of the drive shaft speed and gear ratio. With no slip they should agree. The system is outlined diagrammatically in Figure 6.7.

As the brake pedal is pressed, so the wheel will begin to slow down. Slippage then starts to occur and so the pulse outputs from the wheel and drive shaft no longer agree. At a predetermined difference the brake pressure will be reduced, so allowing the wheel to spin more freely. This in turn will produce a closer match of speeds and so the brake pressure will automatically be increased again – assuming the driver's foot is still on the brake pedal. The whole system is controlled by microprocessors in the Electronic Control Unit (ECU).

Figure 6.7
Wheel slip detection system

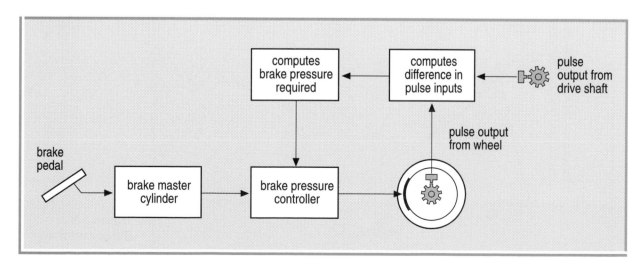

Q11 Write a few notes, with explanatory diagrams, outlining a number of methods by which the number of rotations each second could be measured. ◆

Electromagnetism is normally used for this task, and in Section 8 you will be able to look at the physics of two of its most commonly used techniques.

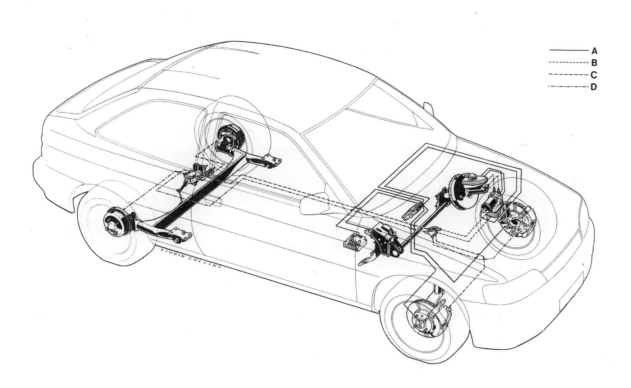

Anti-lock braking system on a Ford vehicle

Achievements

After working through this section you should be able to:

- apply the theory of the thermal transfer of energy

- define and use the coefficient of sliding friction

- describe a molecular model for the friction between moving surfaces

- devise a practical way of determining those factors that contribute to efficient braking

- state the advantages of having (i) metal and (ii) carbon fibre disc brakes

- calculate a stopping distance given data on a vehicle and the road surface with which it is in contact

- investigate and report on the relationships between the factors affecting stopping distance during braking

- understand and explain the principles of anti-lock braking

- suggest methods by which speeds of rotation may be measured.

Glossary

Adhesion   The process that acts at the surface between two different substances and results in unlike molecules attracting each other and so causing the two surfaces to 'stick' together. This is what glues and adhesives do. The adhesive force is the force with which two surfaces attract each other.

Coefficient of friction   The ratio of the frictional force to the normal reaction. There are two coefficients for friction when one object is sliding over another: (i) dynamic or sliding friction and (ii) static or limiting friction. There is also a coefficient for rolling friction. The usual symbol for the coefficient of friction is μ and it has no units.

Conduction (thermal)   The process by which energy is transferred (i) in a gas, where collisions aid energy exchange between molecules, (ii) in metals, through energy exchange due to the motions of electrons, and (iii) in other solids (including metals) and liquids, through vibrational energy exchange between neighbouring molecules.

Convection   The process in a gas or liquid in which heating will cause the fluid to become less dense, float upwards and so transfer energy away from its source.

Ductile   Capable of being moulded, pressed into shape or drawn out into a wire.

Fading   A property of friction brakes in which the braking force decreases during the braking process. It is thought to be due to liquid resin oozing to the surface and reducing molecular contact between the brake pads and the brake disc.

Friction   The resistance one object experiences when moving over another. It is thought to be mainly to do with the attraction of molecules for each other over short distances. It is reduced by the presence of liquids between the objects' surfaces.

Longitudinal   Running lengthwise.

Radiation   The process in which energy is transferred by electromagnetic waves. The best example is energy transfer from the Sun, neither conduction nor convention being possible through the near vacuum of space.

Stiff   Capable of resisting bending.

Strong   Capable of resisting large forces before breaking.

Thermal conductor   *See Conduction (thermal)*.

Tough   Capable of resisting cracking.

Transverse   Acting in a crosswise direction.

Wheel slip   A measure of the degree to which a wheel is locked or not rotating: 100% wheel slip is a totally locked wheel that is sliding over the surface; 0% wheel slip indicates complete rotation of the wheel but no movement over the surface at all.

Answers to Ready to Study test

R1

(a) Biscuit: stiff, brittle.

(b) Steel: tough, stiff, strong.

(c) Nylon: tough, strong.

R2

(a) To the left.

(b) To the left – friction acts to oppose the motion.

R3

Examples (a) and (c) make use of friction.

R4

Only property (c) is true for all forces.

R5

Student A gave the best estimates.

R6

(a) Appropriate words are 'transferred', 'solids' and 'convection'.

(b) Radiation does not depend on a material medium so it is the method of energy transfer that will operate over empty space.

R7

(a) She lives between 6.428 and 6.432 km away from college by her measurements.

(b) Any journey will be difficult to repeat precisely. On a second attempt she may take a corner more tightly or walk around a

parked car. A human pace is about 1 m long, so Gyda is claiming that she can measure to an accuracy of 2 paces in 6430, which is an uncertainty of 0.03%. We would find that hard to believe if she did in fact pace it out. But if she used a laser tape measure then it becomes more believable.

Answers to questions in the text

Q1

By spinning in the air the whole surface of the disc can constantly be cooled by a 'new' volume of air in contact with it. The processes involved would be those that you met in your GCSE science or physics course – conduction and convection. In the process of conduction, the molecules of air in contact with the heated disc would have energy transferred to them in collisions with the molecules of the disc and so, in moving away from the disc, would take some of the disc's energy with them. If the disc remained still, some of these air molecules would, following collisions with each other, come back and hit the disc, so warming it up again. Spinning the disc is likely to result in more slow-moving air molecules coming into contact with the disc. In the process of convection the air close to the disc will be warmed and expand, so making it less dense than the surrounding air. Being less dense, this air will float upwards in the colder surrounding air and so transfer energy away from the disc. By spinning the disc this less dense air is moved away from the disc more quickly and so cools it more quickly. If the disc got *very* hot indeed then quite a lot of energy would be transferred away from it as electromagnetic radiation.

Q2

Carbon fibre is a less dense material than steel and so this makes the brake discs lighter. A less massive vehicle can be accelerated more quickly and also uses less fuel. Carbon fibre is a black material. As you may know, black materials are very good radiators of energy, hence they will cool down more quickly. However, you may also know that black materials are good absorbers of radiation and so think that these carbon fibre discs ought to remain at the same temperature all the time – first radiating energy and then re-absorbing it. The key factors to bear in mind are that a material will be a *net radiator* of energy if it is hot compared with its surroundings and a *net absorber* of energy if it is cold compared with its surroundings. Also, steel disks are easily overheated. They may then deform causing reduced braking efficiency and a juddering of the vehicle.

Q3

When you are trying to move something from a stationary position it is likely that the object has settled down on to the lower surface and so have made more close molecular contacts. The more close molecular contacts there are, the larger the force needed to overcome them. Movement will tend to reduce the opportunity for settling, so less molecular contacts will be made and less force is needed to keep the object moving. In addition, sometimes movement may bring about some heating of the materials which, if melting can occur, will bring a liquid layer between the materials and so reduce the molecular contact between their surfaces.

Q4

Cast iron is cheap to make and is strong under compression. Being a metal it is also a relatively good thermal conductor and so transfers energy away from the brake pads to the disc fairly quickly. Failure to keep the pads cool would soon result in brake fade.

Q5

The wire, being made of metal, is a much better thermal conductor than the resin and asbestos (or its substitute) into which it is bonded. This helps transfer energy more quickly away from the brake pad and so keep it cooler. Cooling the pads should prevent brake fade.

Q6

Slicks will place large areas of the tyre in direct contact with the road surface. The warmer the day, the softer the tyre, and so the more the tyre will settle on to the road surface. The effect of this is to increase the molecular contact between the surfaces and, in turn, the friction between them. This is fine on a hot dry day but, on a cold wet day the greatest need is to force the surface water away from the tyre, as this reduces the molecular contact between the tyre and the road. The tread on tyres is designed to force this water away.

Q7

The braking distance is (a) directly proportional to the trolley's mass, (b) inversely proportional to the braking force, and (c) directly proportional to the trolley's initial speed squared. For example: if the trolley's mass was doubled, then the braking distance would also be doubled; if the braking force was doubled, then the braking distance would be halved; if the trolley's initial speed was doubled, then the braking distance would be quadrupled. (*Note:* Each assumes that all other factors have remained unchanged.)

Q8

The estimated speed will be a lower value because when the brakes are applied there will be a short period of rapid deceleration before the wheels lock and the skid occurs. The estimated speed will be that at which the skid begins.

Q9

(a)

$$13.4\,\mathrm{m\,s^{-1}} = \sqrt{2 \times 0.8 \times 9.81\,\mathrm{N\,kg^{-1}} \times s}$$

giving

$$s = 11.44\,\mathrm{m}$$

$$= 1 \times 10^1\,\mathrm{m}\ \text{(to one significant figure)}$$

(b)

$$13.4\,\mathrm{m\,s^{-1}} = \sqrt{2 \times 0.4 \times 9.81\,\mathrm{N\,kg^{-1}} \times s}$$

giving

$$s = 22.88\,\mathrm{m}$$

$$= 2 \times 10^1\,\mathrm{m}\ \text{(to one significant figure)}$$

Q10

The weight of the masses hung on the end of the string and the frictional force are equal, since there is no resultant force, and therefore we can deduce the size of the frictional force.

Q11

There are many possible methods, but here are two simple ones:

(i) A light gate/photocell could activate timing when a section of the wheel/gear breaks its light beam. The number of times it breaks the beam each second is equal to the number of rotations each second.

(ii) A magnet attached to the wheel/gear could close a small reed switch each time it passes. If that reed switch was connected to a timing circuit then you could see how many times it closed in a second, which is equal to the number of rotations each second.

CASE STUDY: BETTER SKIS FOR ARTIFICIAL SLOPES

Jennie Constable

This section consists of an extended exercise; it is longer than the explorations that we have presented to you so far. You are given data from a real investigation and taken through an analysis of those data. The data have been adapted from an article in *Aerospace Dynamics* (Constable, 1984) a technical journal of British Aerospace plc. It dealt with the research undertaken by Jennie Constable, then an A-level student at Longdean School in Hemel Hempstead, studying physics, chemistry and mathematics. The analysis follows her original research.

The objectives of this work are to give you a chance to reinforce your recent learning about friction and, more importantly, to help you gain skills in data analysis and comprehension exercises. (*Note:* You need to have studied Section 6 before beginning this section.)

Often a situation that uses quite basic physics can seem impenetrable at first because of the amount of circumstantial detail that you have to absorb. We hope that you won't find this example too obscure but enjoy the search for that elusive ideal material for a dry ski slope along with Jennie.

Following her A-levels, Jennie joined British Aerospace as an undergraduate apprentice and went on to read engineering at Cambridge University. Her project involved approximately 300 hours of work spread over four terms. It was awarded the Special Tribology Prize by the Institution of Mechanical Engineers and was selected by the British Association for the Advancement of Science to represent the UK at the International Science and Engineering Fair at Albuquerque, New Mexico, in May 1983, where it won the second place physics prize.

7.1 The problem

There is little friction between high-density polythene (HDPE) soled skis and snow. This is because of the thin film of water between the ski and the snow produced by heating the snow. This is not, however, the case with artificial dry ski slopes, where skis run over stiff polyvinyl chloride (PVC) bristles like those shown here.

Ski slope bristles

112

The frictional forces are high, leading to a shortened life for ordinary skis (some last only 25 hours), slow runs and rather steep slopes, which may scare beginners. Jenny's research yielded a lot of information and data, eventually leading to proposals for a lower-friction and harder-wearing material with which to sole skis. The questions in this section are based either directly on her data or on data extrapolated from it.

 Why will the slopes need to be steep if the frictional forces are high?

So that a skier travels fast enough to be able to manoeuvre in a way similar to moving on snow. If the slope is too shallow they won't move at all.

7.2 Wear testing

The amount of wear exhibited by various ski sole materials in 30 s wear tests and subsequent 10 min wear tests is shown in Table 7.1.

Table 7.1 The results of wear tests for various materials

Material	30 s wear test wear/mm	10 min wear test extra wear/mm
High-density polythene (HDPE)	1.60	3.0
Ultrahigh molecular weight polythene (UHMWPE)	0.14	0.1
Polytetrafluoroethylene (PTFE)	0.26	0.1
Mica-filled PTFE	0.17	*
Graphite-filled PTFE	0.11	0.008
Graphite-and-bronze-filled PTFE	0.17	*
Glass-fibre-filled PTFE	0.28	*
Glass-powder-filled PTFE	0.31	*
Ceramic-filled PTFE	0.13	*
Shamban	0.13	*
Glass cloth coated with PTFE	1.60	*
Kemetal (acetal)	†	0.28
Formica	†	†
Nylon	†	*
Nylatron GS (Nylon with molybdenum disulphide)	†	†

* Eliminated on the basis of other tests.

† No detectable wear.

Which materials showed no detectable wear after 30 s?

Kemetal, Formica, Nylon and Nylatron GS showed no detectable wear after 30 s.

 Which materials showed much more wear than the others?

Glass cloth coated with PTFE and HDPE showed more wear than the others.

Q1   If you could get some small sheets of the ski sole materials, together with some ski slope bristles, explain as fully as you can how *you* would conduct these wear tests. ◆

 Despite its poor performance in the 30 s wear test, HDPE was still given a 10 min wear test. Suggest a reason for doing this.

Two possible reasons are:

(a) The surface layers of the HDPE may have different properties from those lower down.

(b) The material may be altered in some way as the surface is worn away.

 Which materials look promising for use on the soles of skis?

From the tests conducted so far, Formica and Nylatron GS look promising.

 Which materials showed less extra wear in 10 min than they had in the first 30 s?

UHMWPE, PTFE and graphite-filled PTFE showed less extra wear in 10 min than in the first 30 s.

Q2   Suggest why some materials showed less extra wear in 10 min than they had in the first 30 s. ◆

7.3 Static friction test

The force needed to *just* move a loaded 'brush' of ski slope bristles on top of the ski surface was measured. (If the situation were reversed, and you measured the force needed to just move a loaded ski surface on top of the 'brush', the force would be the same.)

Table 7.2 shows the results obtained for PTFE and Formica; these were then plotted to form the graphs shown in Figure 7.1.

Table 7.2 Data for Figure 7.1

Load on 'brush'/N	Force needed to just move 'brush'/N	
	PTFE	Formica
0.00	0.00	0.00
10.00	0.83	1.32
20.00	1.66	2.61
30.00	2.49	3.98
40.00	3.32	5.32
50.00	4.15	6.60
60.00	6.50	8.02
70.00	8.72	9.15
80.00	11.03	10.55
90.00	13.41	12.03
100.00	14.90	13.24
110.00	16.45	14.56
120.00	18.00	15.91

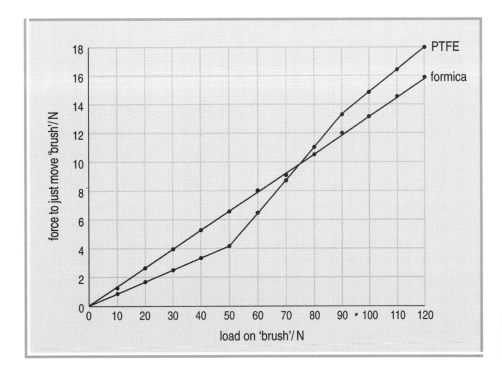

Figure 7.1
Force against load for PTFE and Formica

Q3 Estimate the force needed to just move the 'brush' on the PTFE-soled ski if the load was 35 N. ◆

Q4 Estimate the force needed to just move the 'brush' on the Formica-soled ski if the load was 140 N. ◆

Q5 Which of these estimates, the one for PTFE or the one for Formica, is the most reliable? Explain your reasoning. ◆

The coefficient of static friction, μ_s, is given by the expression

$$\mu_s = \frac{\text{force (N) to just move brush}}{\text{load (N) on brush}}$$

Q6 Using the graphs in Figure 7.1, or the data in Table 7.2, and the above relationship, calculate the average coefficient of static friction for PTFE in the load ranges: (a) 0–50 N, (b) 50–90 N and (c) 90–120 N. ◆

Q7 Using the graphs in Figure 7.1, or the data in Table 7.2, and the above relationship, calculate the average coefficient of static friction for Formica in the load ranges: (a) 0–50 N, (b) 50–90 N and (c) 90–120 N. ◆

Q8 What differences in the average coefficients of static friction do you notice between PTFE and Formica? ◆

Table 7.3 gives the coefficients of static friction for a number of other materials that Jennie tested.

Table 7.3

Material	Coefficients of static friction, μ_s	
	Loads of 0–56 N	Load of 86 N
HDPE	0.122 ± 0.007	0.177 ± 0.009
UHMWPE	0.117 ± 0.004	0.130 ± 0.009
Mica-filled PTFE	0.103 ± 0.001	0.130 ± 0.009
Graphite-filled PTFE	0.118 ± 0.003	0.142 ± 0.009
Graphite-and-bronze-filled PTFE	0.131 ± 0.004	0.130 ± 0.009
Glass-fibre-filled PTFE	0.129 ± 0.006	0.151 ± 0.005
Glass-powder-filled PTFE	0.164 ± 0.006	0.162 ± 0.006
Ceramic-filled PTFE	0.141 ± 0.004	0.165 ± 0.009
Shamban	0.184 ± 0.005	0.197 ± 0.006
Glass cloth coated with PTFE	0.148 ± 0.008	0.194 ± 0.009
Kemetal	0.129 ± 0.002	0.119 ± 0.002
Nylon	0.134 ± 0.003	0.134 ± 0.003
Nylatron GS	0.124 ± 0.003	0.124 ± 0.003

Readings in this form (0.122 ± 0.007 for HDPE, for example) show the degree of accuracy with which the measurements were obtained. The value of μ_s for HDPE lay somewhere between 0.115 and 0.129.

Q9 Which of these materials behave, with regard to their coefficient of static friction, in a similar way to PTFE? Explain your answer. ◆

Q10 Which of these materials behave, with regard to their coefficient of static friction, in a similar way to Formica? Explain your answer. ◆

Seeing how the skis performed in practice was Jennie's next task. The skis were pulled across a level section of dry ski run by means of a forcemeter (also called a spring balance, a Newtonmeter or a dynamometer).

Action on a ski slope

As the skis just began to move the reading on the forcemeter was noted. The coefficient of static friction was then calculated. The results of the experiments are shown in Table 7.4, together with the average and peak values found in the laboratory for loads of 0–56 N (0–50 N for PTFE).

Table 7.4

| Material | Coefficients of static friction, μ_s | | |
| | On ski run | In laboratory | |
	average	average	peak
HDPE	0.134 ± 0.008	0.122 ± 0.007	0.128 ± 0.006
UHMWPE	0.142 ± 0.008	0.117 ± 0.004	0.140 ± 0.007
PTFE	0.108 ± 0.008	0.083 ± 0.001	0.116 ± 0.004
Kemetal	0.120 ± 0.008	0.119 ± 0.002	0.119 ± 0.002
Formica	0.134 ± 0.008	0.134 ± 0.004	0.134 ± 0.004
Nylatron GS	0.121 ± 0.008	0.124 ± 0.006	0.124 ± 0.006

Q11 How well do the laboratory results support the actual static coefficients obtained on the ski run? Explain your answer using the tabulated data. ◆

7.4 Coefficient of sliding, or dynamic, friction

Finally, the coefficient of sliding, or dynamic, friction was measured. This is given by:

$$\text{coefficient of sliding friction } \mu_{\text{sliding}} = \frac{\text{force (N) to move brush steadily}}{\text{load (N) on brush}}$$

These coefficients were obtained indirectly by timing runs down a 30 m dry ski slope. Table 7.5 displays the values alongside the static coefficients obtained on the ski slope. Results were not obtained for UHMWPE or Kemetal.

Table 7.5

Material	Sliding coefficient	Static coefficient
HDPE	0.135 ± 0.009	0.134 ± 0.008
UHMWPE		0.142 ± 0.008
PTFE	0.129 ± 0.009	0.108 ± 0.008
Kemetal		0.120 ± 0.008
Formica	0.139 ± 0.009	0.134 ± 0.008
Nylatron GS	0.118 ± 0.009	0.121 ± 0.008

It is usually expected that the static coefficient will be greater than the sliding coefficient. Table 7.5 shows that experimental results do not always fit in with expectations!

Q12 Which sliding coefficient(s) match well with the static coefficients on the slope? Explain your answer. ◆

Q13 Which sliding coefficient(s) do not match well with the static coefficients on the slope? Explain your answer. ◆

Q14 If Kemetal behaves like Formica, what is its coefficient of sliding friction likely to be? ◆

Q15 If UHMWPE behaves like PTFE, what is its coefficient of sliding friction likely to be? ◆

Q16 If you wanted a fast and hard-wearing material with which to sole skis for use on dry ski slopes what would you choose? Explain your choice. ◆

Achievements

After working through this section you should be able to:

- follow a data analysis based on a student project
- practise using static friction and coefficient of friction, and devise a possible static friction test (but not carry it out)
- evaluate data, including graphical data, taking into account uncertainties in results.

Answers to questions in the text

Q1

There are many possible methods, but a simple one is to arrange the bristles so that they can be mounted on a drill (rather like a polishing mitt). Then have these bristles pressing down on ski sole material with constant pressure for a set period of time. To maintain constant pressure, the ski sole could be placed on bathroom scales and the drill and bristles pushed down on to it so that a fixed force was displayed.

Q2

There is more than one possibility. It may be that the initial wear knocks off the rough surfaces from the bristles making them less abrasive. Alternatively, perhaps properties of the surface of the ski sole material are different from those deeper within it.

Q3

You should have an estimate of around 2.9 N.

Q4

You should have an estimate of around 18.4 N.

Q5

The estimate for PTFE is likely to be the more reliable as the prediction is made by interpolation. Extrapolation is required for the Formica.

Q6

(a) For PTFE the coefficients of static friction remained near enough constant at 0.083 over the range 0–50 N.

(b) Over the range 50–90 N, the values of the coefficients of static friction for each load on the 'brush' were approximately 0.083, 0.108, 0.125, 0.138 and 0.149. These provide an average value of 0.120.

(c) Over the range 90–120 N, the values of the coefficients of static friction for each load on the 'brush' were approximately 0.149, 0.149, 0.150 and 0.150. These provide an average value of 0.150.

Q7

For the Formica, regardless of the load on the 'brush', the coefficient of static friction is always approximately 0.132.

Q8

The coefficients of static friction of Formica are unchanged with the load on the 'brush', whilst those of PTFE change with the load on the 'brush'. With the PTFE the coefficients of static friction remain the same over the range 0–50 N, they then increase steadily over the range 50–90 N, but then stabilize again over the range 90–120 N.

Q9

None of the materials behave like PTFE. The value of the coefficient of static friction of PTFE up to loads on the 'brush' of 50 N remained at 0.08. At a load on the 'brush' of 56 N its coefficient is 0.098. No materials are within this range in the first column of data.

Q10

Just graphite-and-bronze-filled PTFE and Nylon behave like Formica. The former's coefficients are between 0.127 and 0.135 for loads 0–56 N, and between 0.121 and 0.139 for a load of 86 N. Formica had an average coefficient of static friction of 0.132, which falls within these ranges. Similarly for Nylon, with coefficients between 0.131 and 0.137 for loads 0–56 N and 86 N.

Q11

HDPE, Kemetal, Formica and Nylatron GS each have coefficients that match within the uncertainties given. For example, HDPE's coefficient on the ski run was between 0.126 and 0.142. In the laboratory its average coefficient was between 0.115 and 0.129, and its peak was between 0.122 and 0.134. All are within each other's bands of uncertainty. Likewise with the other three materials.

Q12

HDPE, Formica and Nylatron GS have sliding coefficients that match well with their static coefficients. As in Question 11, all their values lie within each other's bands of uncertainty.

Q13

Only PTFE's sliding and static coefficients do not match well, of those we have data for. PTFE has a sliding coefficient of friction between 0.120 and 0.138. Its static coefficient of friction is between 0.100 and 0.116. There is no overlap of these bands of uncertainty.

Q14

Its coefficient of sliding friction is likely to be somewhere in the range 0.112 to 0.128, having both sliding and static coefficients very similar to each other.

Q15

One cannot be precise, but a value greater than 0.150 for UHMWPE's sliding coefficient would be expected. PTFE's sliding coefficient was well beyond its static coefficient.

Q16

Nylatron GS looks the best choice. Its sliding coefficient of friction is low, though similar to PTFE's taking into consideration the uncertainty of the data. However, PTFE did not do so well in the wear test.

You might think that a non-contact brake is a contradiction in terms. However, it is only non-contact from the point of view of not having surfaces rubbing together. There is contact, but it is between magnetic fields. Figure 8.1 shows the construction of a non-contact brake.

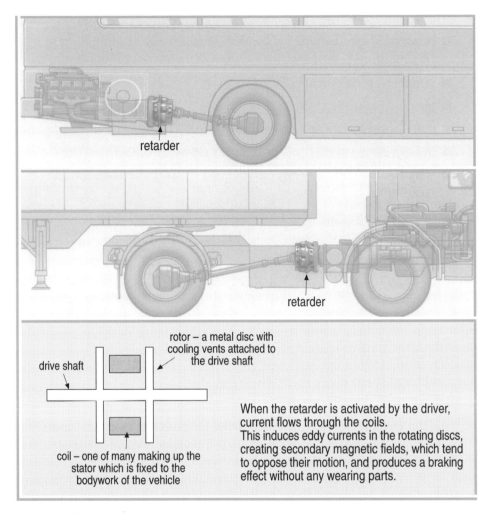

retarder

retarder

rotor – a metal disc with cooling vents attached to the drive shaft

drive shaft

coil – one of many making up the stator which is fixed to the bodywork of the vehicle

When the retarder is activated by the driver, current flows through the coils.
This induces eddy currents in the rotating discs, creating secondary magnetic fields, which tend to oppose their motion, and produces a braking effect without any wearing parts.

Figure 8.1 A non-contact brake (known as a retarder or eddy current brake)

READY TO STUDY TEST

Before studying this section you should be able to:

- describe the processes of conduction, convection and radiation as means of transferring energy (considered in Section 6)
- describe the mechanism thought to cause brake fading (covered in Section 6)
- connect up electrical circuits
- use and read electrical meters
- read stopwatches and other timers
- measure the speeds and/or kinetic energy of objects
- state the difference between direct (d.c.) and alternating (a.c.) current
- draw the 'catapult' field of a conductor (wire) carrying a current, placed in a magnetic field and perpendicular to that field.

QUESTIONS

R1   A current is passed through a fixed solenoid coil. The left end of the coil behaves like the north pole of a magnet. What could you do to make it a south pole?

R2   A second coil is connected only through an ammeter to make a circuit. Describe as many ways as possible in which you could use a bar magnet and the coil to produce a short burst of electric current.

R3   Figure 8.2 shows two electric currents. Draw the shape of the magnetic field that each of these currents creates and add arrows to show the directions of the fields.

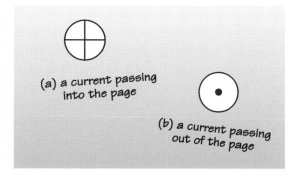

(a) a current passing into the page

(b) a current passing out of the page

Figure 8.2

The type of brake that we are discussing in this section is shown in Figure 8.1. It is known as a retarder or **eddy current** brake. Two discs, called **rotors**, are fixed to, and rotate with, the transmission shaft – the drive shaft that makes the wheels turn. Between the rotors is the **stator**, the non-rotating part, containing a series of coils making up an electromagnet. An electric current is fed to the coils in such a way that adjacent coils have reversed magnetic fields. The discs rotating in these fields have electric currents **induced** in them. These currents are known as eddy currents.

From your earlier work on electromagnetism you will know that the movement of a coil of wire in a magnetic field generates an electric current in it (the dynamo effect). Electric currents in turn produce magnetic fields. Electromagnetism is dealt with more fully in other SLIPP units, such as the unit on fields (*Physics Phones Home*) and the unit on flow (*Physics of Flow*). If you think of the metal discs as containing lots of wire loops within themselves, then you can probably visualize the generation of lots of currents within the discs and some quite strong magnetic fields. It is the interaction of the fields of the coils and the discs that causes the slowing down or braking.

Lenz's law (which is really an alternative way of stating the law of conservation of energy) states that:

> The direction of the current induced in a conductor by a changing magnetic field is such that its own magnetic field opposes the change.

LENZ'S LAW

The direction of the current induced in a conductor by a changing magnetic field is such that its own magnetic field opposes the change.

In this case, the currents in the metal discs produce magnetic fields that interact with those of the coils of the stator to slow down the wheels.

The discs make no contact with any solid surface so no wear takes place. This means that the expensive replacing of brake pads is kept to a minimum. Conventional brake pads are still needed, but only for the final slow-speed braking and for parking.

This system involves an energy transfer so the discs will got hot. As they are made of conductive material they cool quite quickly; often air is ducted in to help the cooling process.

What might happen if the discs were not cooled?

> They might expand and then jam up against the fixed magnets (stators).

You may have wondered why adjacent coils were powered to produce reversed magnetic fields. Can you remember conducting experiments in which magnets were pushed into and out of coils connected to galvanometers? (A galvanometer is a very sensitive ammeter.) As the magnet was moved, so a current was indicated on the galvanometer. The key is that induced currents are produced whenever there is a *change* of magnetic field. Now think of what happens as the discs rotate through these magnetic fields.

Why are adjacent coils arranged to have reversed magnetic fields?

With adjacent coils having reversed magnetic fields the discs (rotors) will be *constantly* moving through *changing* magnetic fields. Changing magnetic fields will induce currents in the discs, which, in turn, will produce magnetic fields slowing down their rotation.

Instead of arranging the connections to the coils to produce reversed magnetic fields, the unit could be fed with alternating current (a.c.).

Q1 Explain (a) how coils fed with alternating current would produce a similar effect to having adjacent coils arranged with reversed magnetic fields and (b) whether the brake would work better with high-frequency a.c. magnetic fields. ◆

The rules of the game

A larger induced current is produced if

■ the conductor is moved faster through the magnetic field

■ the magnetic field through which the conductor moves is stronger.

These 'rules' can be summarized more fully in terms of Faraday's laws and are considered in the SLIPP unit on electromagnetic fields (*Physics Phones Home*) and the unit *Physics of Flow*. It is possible to use this braking technique for both linear and rotational set-ups. The Advanced Passenger Train (APT), the one that had its passenger compartment designed to lean over on bends, initially considered a linear eddy current brake design. The rails were the conductors. As you will see in this section, many coaches and heavy lorries use the technique to slow down the rotation of their drive shafts. Many coin in the slot machines also make use of eddy current braking to help them determine the type of coin inserted. We suggest a number of investigatory activities that you may wish to consider and follow up in Exploration 8.1.

 Exploration 8.1   Eddy current braking

100-120 MINUTES

Apparatus:

◆ linear air track, vehicle and accessories   ◆ air blower   ◆ light gate   ◆ various metal plates and discs   ◆ computer with interface and timing/velocity measuring software or two electronic stopclocks   ◆ rotating eddy current braking equipment as shown in Figure 8.4

Investigate the factors that affect the braking, i.e. how they affect it and why you think they affect it in these ways. You could then follow this up with recommendations for the design of a braking system thinking about which variables would be the key ones and why. Two possible arrangements of equipment are outlined in Figures 8.3 and 8.4.

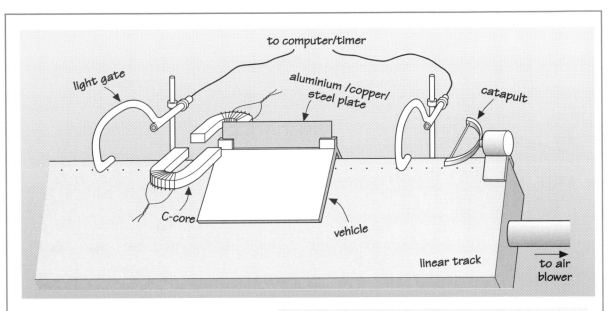

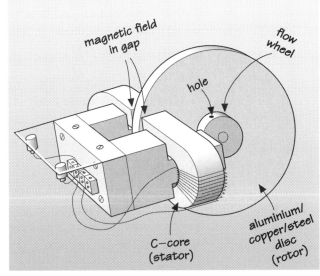

Figure 8.3
A linear system

Figure 8.4
A rotating system

Hints and tips

Variables to consider:

- length of conductive plate or diameter of disc

- thickness of conductive plate or disc

- **conductivity** (or **resistivity**) of material from which plate or disc is made

- magnetic field strength in vicinity of plate or disc, in turn related to: (i) current in coils; (ii) number of turns on coils; (iii) closeness of C-cores (*Note:* Magnetic field strength is most easily measured with calibrated Hall probes)

- whether an a.c. or d.c. field is applied and, if a.c., its frequency.

Using the linear system

This enables you to analyse the change of kinetic energy of the linear air track vehicle after it has passed through the magnetic field.

Using the rotating system

This enables you to measure the time the disc takes to stop rotating after being given a standard torque to start it off. (If you have already studied the use of **angular kinetic energy** and **moments of inertia**, then analysis of the change in angular kinetic energy might also be a fruitful way forward.)

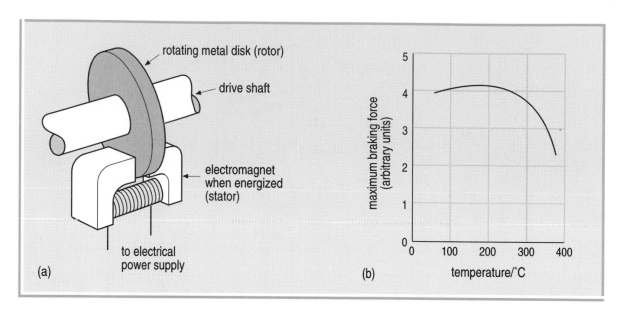

Figure 8.5
Eddy current
braking

Many heavy lorries and coaches are fitted with brakes that utilize electrical eddy currents. A simplified system of eddy current braking is shown in Figure 8.5(a).

Q2 (a) Explain why eddy currents are being produced in the metal disc.

(b) Explain how these eddy currents result in the braking of the disc.

(c) Suggest one desirable property of the disc that will enable large currents to be induced in it. ◆

Q3 The graph in Figure 8.5(b) illustrates the variation with temperature of the maximum braking force obtained with one type of friction brake. By reference to this graph, state one disadvantage of a friction brake and explain why this is more likely to be a problem with a heavy lorry than with a car. ◆

Q4 (a) What becomes of the energy transferred from the vehicle when eddy current braking is applied?

(b) Outline two ways in which this transferred energy is subsequently dissipated to the environment. ◆

Q5 Eddy current brakes tend to be used to brake from relatively high speeds.

(a) Why are they more effective at higher speeds?

(b) Why could this system not be used as a parking brake? ◆

Q6 Explain one way in which an increased eddy current braking effect could be produced at a specific speed. ◆

Achievements

After working through this section you should be able to:

- describe magnetism in terms of fields, poles and electromagnets
- describe the basic principles of electromagnetic induction and the production of eddy currents
- investigate and report on eddy current braking
- make recommendations for the design of an eddy current braking system.

Glossary

Angular kinetic energy Unit: joule (J). The energy associated with a rotating object. It is calculated from

$$\frac{1}{2}\left(\text{moment of inertia} \times \text{angular velocity}^2\right).$$

Angular kinetic energy is a scalar quantity.

Conductivity Unit: siemens per metre (S m^{-1}). A term relating how easily electric current will flow through a specified sample of material. A material of high conductivity will allow large currents to flow through the sample. Conductivity is discussed in more detail in Section 9.3.

Eddy current An electric current brought about in a spinning disc. It is due to the rotation of the disc and a series of conductors in a magnetic field.

Induced A word used in conjunction with current or electromotive force (e.m.f.) to refer to a phenomenon brought about by the motion of a conductor in a magnetic field or a change of a magnetic field around a conductor.

Moment of inertia Unit: kilogram metre squared (kg m^2). A quantity involving both the mass and its distribution within an object about an axis of rotation. Moment of inertia is a scalar quantity.

Resistivity Unit: ohm (Ω). This is the reciprocal of conductivity and is referred to later in Section 9.3.

Rotor The rotating part of an electrical machine.

Stator The part of an electrical machine that includes the non-rotating magnets. Stationary, meaning to remain still, has the same word stem.

Answers to Ready to Study test

R1

Reversing the direction of the current would achieve this.

R2

Line up the magnet so that it can move into the centre of the coil. Any movement of the coil towards the magnet, or of the magnet towards the coil, will produce an electric current. The faster the movement the larger the effect. Similarly, rotation of the coil near the magnet, or of the magnet near the end of the coil, will also produce a current.

R3

See Figure 8.6.

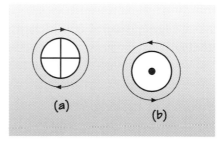

Figure 8.6

Answers to questions in the text

Q1

(a) If the coils were fed with alternating current they would be *constantly* producing *changing* magnetic fields. So, induced currents will be produced, which, in turn, will produce magnetic fields slowing down the discs' rotation.

(b) The higher the frequency the better, as long as the strength of the electric current supplied is maintained. A faster rate of change of magnetic field will induce larger currents in the discs. Larger currents in the discs will produce stronger magnetic forces to slow down their rotation more quickly.

Q2

(a) The disc could be looked upon as a series of conductors all moving in a magnetic field. As such, currents will be induced in them, as they would be in any moving conductor.

(b) The eddy current produces its own magnetic field. This field interacts with the electromagnet's field. The direction of the eddy current's field is such that the interaction opposes motion. This is an example of a force on a current in a field.

(c) The disc should be thick and made of a material that has a high electrical conductivity (i.e. low resistivity).

Q3

At high temperatures its braking force reduces. A lorry will have more energy to transfer in braking than a car, and so more heating is likely. The friction brake would therefore reach a higher temperature in a lorry than in a car travelling at the same speed.

Q4

(a) Transferred energy initially heats up the disc.

(b) This energy is mainly transferred to the environment by convection and radiation. Such a system is frequently air cooled, sometimes by forced convection. Air is not a good thermal conductor and so energy transfer by conduction is relatively unimportant.

Q5

(a) The faster the conductor (the disc) moves through the magnetic field, the greater the induced current and the greater the braking effect.

(b) Without any movement of the disc there would be no induced current and so no braking effect at all.

Q6

There are a number of ways of doing this, they include: (i) increase the strength of the magnetic field – feed a larger current into it, lessen the distance between the magnet's poles or increase the number of turns on its coils; (ii) have a more conductive disc; (iii) feed high-frequency alternating currents into the electromagnet.

Many of the aspects of the physical world you are studying have the potential to act for both good and ill. In some contexts they can be very useful; elsewhere they just seem a nuisance. Friction is an example – without it we couldn't walk very far, yet whenever we run any machinery we have to apply expensive lubricating oils to overcome it.

A similar property, associated with moving fluids, is the subject of two of the topics in this section. As the basis for fluid brakes it is beneficial; as it appears in aerodynamic drag it has many disadvantages. And when the movement of fluids results in electrostatic separation the outcomes could be disastrous. This is the subject of the third topic in this section: 'Safety with fuels'.

An understanding of these resistive forces and their effects allows us to make the most of them when needed, or to reduce them as much as possible by careful design.

 Can you think of other examples of properties with Jekyll and Hyde characteristics?

Electrical resistance is necessary for ohmic heating, but it puts up the costs of transporting energy. Radioactivity is another example, and you probably can think of several more.

READY TO STUDY TEST

Before studying this section you should be able to:

- use the following terms and their associated formulae: 'work', 'energy' (in particular 'kinetic energy' and 'potential energy'), 'power', 'mass', 'volume', 'density', 'momentum', 'current', 'potential difference' and 'resistance'

- draw force diagrams showing drag and friction forces opposing any change of motion

- explain ionization on the basis of the structure of atoms and molecules and understand its contribution to the conduction of electric currents

- define resistance from $R = \dfrac{V}{I}$ and measure resistance using a simple circuit

- state the connection between resistance and the length and cross-sectional area of a conductor

- write down and use Newton's second law of motion (considered in Section 4)

- find the amount of energy transferred to a mass of a material for a given rise in temperature using the relationship:

energy transfer = mass × specific heat capacity
× temperature change

Skim through this section and talk to your teacher about possible routes and choices.

To succeed with the explorations in Section 9.3 'Safety with fuels' you need to understand electrical conduction, at least at the level of GCSE science. Our purpose is to show you how to overcome the dangers involved in transporting fuels safely by applying an understanding of electrical conduction.

Now answer the following questions to see if you can also apply these ideas. Don't take a long time, just run through them with a fellow student to refresh the parts of physics that you will need. It is more important that you recall previous work than that you produce a neat piece of finished work.

QUESTIONS

R1 Electrical resistance is an important physical quantity. You may have carried out an experiment to measure resistance.

(a) Draw a diagram of the circuit that you would use.

(b) Explain how you would use your experimental data to calculate the value of the resistance. Give the units of all quantities.

R2 You will probably have had electrical current explained to you in terms of the movement of charge.

(a) Describe atomic structure in terms of particles and the charges that they carry.

(b) When an electrical current flows in solids, which particles are the most likely to be involved?

(c) Ionization contributes to the conduction of electricity in fluids. What is the process known as ionization?

R3 A wire of length 2 m has a resistance of 0.02 ohm.

(a) The wire is cut in half. What is the resistance of each piece of wire?

(b) The two pieces of wire are then placed side by side to make a 1 m wire that is double the thickness of the original, what is the resistance of this combination?

R4 A circuit is set up like the one in Figure 9.13 towards the end of this section and readings are taken. What is the effect of replacing the voltmeter with one of considerably lower resistance?

R5 Any equation used in physics can be balanced for its units alone. This is one way of checking that it is likely to work. Confirm that the following equation is balanced as far as its units are concerned

power = force × velocity

R6 A metal plate with area A moves through water at velocity v. Show that the volume of water displaced in a time t is given by

volume = $A\,v\,t$

R7 The metal mercury has a density of 13 600 kg m^{-3}.

(a) What volume is needed to give a mass of 680 000 kg?

(b) What is the mass of a volume of 2.5 m^3?

(c) Mercury's specific heat capacity is 139 J kg K^{-1}. How much energy needs to be transferred to a mass of 1.5 kg of mercury to raise its temperature by 3 K?

9.1 Fluid brake

The most well-known example of a **fluid brake** (liquid or gas brake) is the parachute, which is used to brake a vehicle, such as a spacecraft or a drag racer, or a skydiver. The parachute uses air as the braking fluid. Another air brake is used on some lifts to smooth both acceleration and braking. The Harrier jump-jet has a very simple air brake on its underside at the rear as well as a parachute. A liquid brake, known as a **hydrokinetic brake**, was developed for the Advanced Passenger Train.

We can explain how braking occurs in these systems by looking at changes in momentum. A force between the vehicle and the fluid causes a change of momentum of the fluid and consequently of the vehicle too. The parachute's canopy has to accelerate a mass of air that gets trapped in it; the blades of a rotating air brake or hydrokinetic brake will have to accelerate air or liquid respectively.

 Give an equation linking force with a change of momentum.

Force = rate of change of momentum.

The vehicle and fluid interact during braking in a way that increases the momentum of the fluid and at the same time reduces the momentum of the vehicle by an equal amount.

You may have heard about the paddle-wheel designed by James Prescott Joule to establish the link between work done and energy transferred. It was really a hydrokinetic brake, so you should not be surprised that the water in the containing vessel that he used warmed up a little.

Look at the diagram of Joule's paddle-wheel apparatus in Figure 9.1. How do you think he arranged for work to be done? How did he know that energy had been transferred?

The falling weights did work and the temperature of the water rose, indicating that energy had been transferred to it from the paddles.

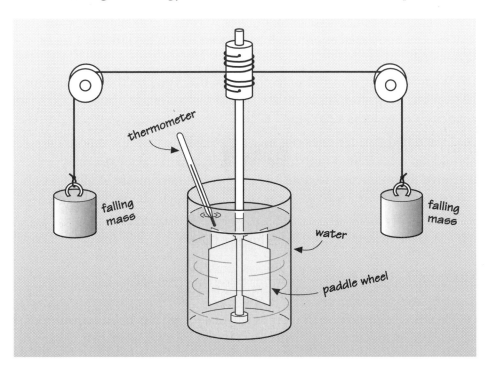

Figure 9.1
Joule's paddle-wheel apparatus

JAMES PRESCOTT JOULE (1818–89)

James Joule was born near Manchester, the second son of a brewer. At the age of seventeen he was a pupil of John Dalton, the founder of scientific atomic theory. Whilst he just loved experimenting, part of his motivation for investigating the link between work and energy was probably to make the brewery engines more efficient and so cheaper to operate. He is recorded as having spent part of his honeymoon measuring the differences between the temperatures at the top and bottom of waterfalls with his wife looking on from their carriage! If you are interested in this area of the history of science then as well as looking up James Joule, also look up Julius Robert Mayer (1814–78), Benjamin Thompson – later Count Rumford (1753–1814) and William Thomson – later Lord Kelvin (1824–1907).

James Joule adapted and refined his equipment over a number of years so that eventually, in 1878, energy transfers that he could not control or account for were minimal. Analysis of the data from his paddle-wheel experiments then showed the link between the energy transferred to the water, paddles, etc., so heating them up, and the change of gravitational potential energy of the falling masses (or work done by them). Today we assume them to be equal to each other, but that had not been realized before Joule's experiments.

You would find it impossible to get the expected rise in temperature in the sort of equipment that you could devise at school or college. In addition, James Joule was able to take many other energy transfers into account, which you would find difficult at this stage.

Q1 Imagine James Joule on his honeymoon at a 100 m high waterfall. Consider just 1 kg of water falling vertically to the bottom.

(a) If the gravitational field strength, g, is 10 N kg^{-1}, calculate how much gravitational potential energy will have been transferred in this 1 kg of water's fall.

(b) What is the greatest rise in temperature that you could expect this mass of water to have after impact at the foot of the waterfall? The specific heat capacity s of water is 4200 J kg^{-1} K^{-1}.

(c) In reality the water does not heat up anywhere near the amount you should have calculated in (b). Indeed, Joule had to have extremely sensitive thermometers to note any change of temperature at all. If it only rose in temperature by 0.04°C, calculate how much energy had been transferred to heat it up.

(d) Calculate the efficiency of this energy transfer.

Efficiency is defined as $\dfrac{\text{useful energy transferred}}{\text{total energy transferred}} \times 100\%$.

(e) To where else do you think most of this energy has been transferred? ◆

 Exploration 9.1   Investigating fluid brakes

Apparatus:

◆ cork ◆ knitting needle ◆ glass tubing ◆ cardboard ◆ Plasticine ◆ thread
◆ glass container ◆ pulley system with selection of small masses ◆ stiff plastic sheet
◆ linear air track with vehicle and accessories ◆ air blower ◆ light gate
◆ computer with interface and timing/velocity measuring software or two electronic stopclocks ◆ thread

Design and construct a fluid brake and investigate the factors that affect the braking and how they affect it. Think about why they affect it in these ways. You could follow up this activity with recommendations for the design of a braking system for a particular purpose. Some possible arrangements of equipment for investigating a fluid brake are shown in Figures 9.2–9.4.

Hints and tips

Your choice of fluid will be limited to water or air in most laboratories. Two of the arrangements of apparatus illustrated are for use in air, the other is for water.

Possible variables

Rotating vane version: area and number of blades; shape of blades; angle of blades; time of fall of falling mass of Plasticine.

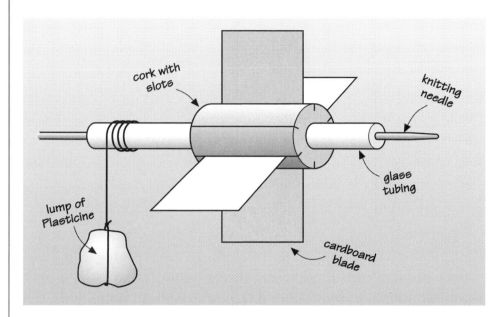

Figure 9.2

Linear air track version: area of brake; angle of brake; time to pass through light gate; change of velocity; change of kinetic energy; change of momentum.

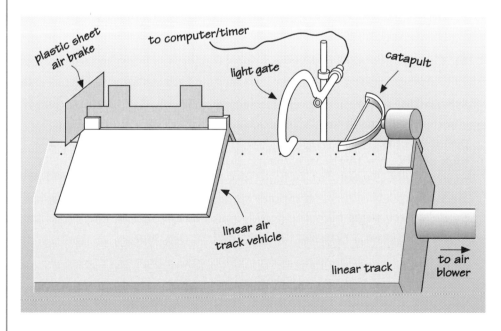

Figure 9.3

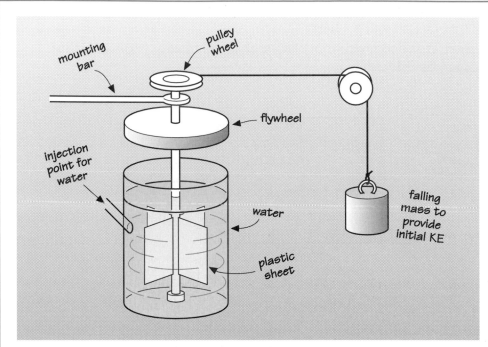

Figure 9.4

Liquid brake: area and number of blades; shape of blades; volume of water injected per second; time to stop rotating; initial speed of rotation or initial torque applied.

Agree with your fellow students how you are going to share your conclusions, as one person cannot possibly cover all the angles of this exploration. Do you all want written reports or are you going to bring everything to a report-back session and talk about the conclusions?

9.2 Aerodynamic drag

Streamlining was first applied to racing cars in the late 1920s and then to some private cars in the 1930s. Today, the high cost of fuel and the polluting effects of its by-products ensure that vehicle designers put a high priority on streamlining, as it reduces fuel consumption. Models representing a possible design are tested, either in wind tunnels if they are real models or using computer simulations if they are mathematical models. How large might the aerodynamic **drag** force be and on what might it depend? To answer this we need an equation.

Some theory

Consider a rectangular plate of area A travelling through still air with a velocity v. In time t it will travel a distance of vt through a box-shaped space whose volume is given by vtA. As it does so it will cause a volume of air vtA to move at velocity v. If the density of this air is ρ (rho), then the mass of air moved will be given by ρvtA (mass = density × volume). Hence the momentum (mass × velocity) gained by the air is $\rho vtA \times v$ or $\rho v^2 tA$. As the force on the plate can be calculated from the rate of change of momentum of the air (another way of stating Newton's second law $F = ma$ – in fact the way he stated it) we have:

$$\text{drag force on plate} = \frac{\rho v^2 t A}{t}$$

$$= \rho v^2 A \tag{9.1}$$

However, when we apply this theory to real vehicles we find that the situation is not that simple. First, most of the air will be deflected fairly smoothly past the vehicle, though with some churning of the air called **turbulence**, particularly at the rear of the vehicle, and second, the area in the equation will not be the surface area of the vehicle but the effective area presented normally to the air flow.

So we need to modify Equation (9.1). This yields an aerodynamic drag force of $\frac{1}{2} C_D \rho v^2 S$, where S is the effective area presented normally to the air flow and C_D is the drag coefficient of the vehicle (a constant that depends on the vehicle's shape and surface characteristics). Most modern cars have drag coefficients around 0.34.

 In the modified equation, which variables can be controlled by a car designer to achieve a low drag force?

The product $C_D \times S$ is determined by the shape, size and profile of the car. The air density is beyond human control and the velocity is determined solely by the driver.

Q2 A car is quoted as having a drag coefficient of 0.34 and effective frontal area presented to the air flow of 2.0 m². Assume that the density of the air is 1.2 kg m⁻³ and that the air was initially still.

(a) Calculate the aerodynamic drag at (i) 10 m s⁻¹, (ii) 20 m s⁻¹, (iii) 30 m s⁻¹ and (iv) 40 m s⁻¹.

(b) Show that the power required to overcome this aerodynamic drag is given by

power to overcome drag = drag force ¥ velocity of vehicle

(c) Calculate the power required to overcome the aerodynamic drag at each of the velocities quoted in (a).

(d) There are a number of other forces opposing the motion of a vehicle: rolling mechanical resistance; brake drag and mechanical losses; drag caused by the need to feed air into the vehicle for cooling, ventilation and combustion. If all these combine with aerodynamic drag to form a total resistance to motion of 1200 N and the maximum power output of the vehicle is 60 kW, calculate the highest velocity attainable. ◆

As we said earlier, streamlining can reduce fuel consumption. In the following question you will be asked to explore the link between design and fuel economy, and then to take a critical look at a salesperson's comment about the relative merits of three cars.

Q3 The factor C_D is known as the drag coefficient and has no units. Its value depends on the shape and styling of a vehicle. A sleek shape often gives a low value for C_D. S is the area of the vehicle when viewed head-on, i.e. the frontal area. See Figure 9.5.

Figure 9.5

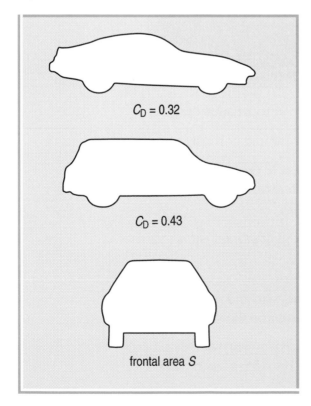

$C_D = 0.32$

$C_D = 0.43$

frontal area S

Table 9.1 gives some data relating ($C_D \times S$) to 'distance travelled on 1 litre of fuel' for vehicles travelling at 70 mph in the same road conditions.

(a) Draw a graph of ($C_D \times S$) against 'distance travelled on 1 litre of fuel'.

(b) Without plotting any further points on the graph, what do you consider is the approximate relationship between ($C_D \times S$) and 'distance travelled on 1 litre of fuel'?

(c) Over the next few years it is hoped that the distance travelled on 1 litre of fuel will be increased by making ($C_D \times S$) smaller. Table 9.2 shows what it is thought might be possible.

(i) Copy the table out and then, using your graph or another suitable method, complete the column 'Distance travelled on 1 litre of fuel'.

(ii) Comment on the reliability of the values you have put into the table.

Table 9.1

Vehicle	$C_D \times S/m^2$	Distance travelled on 1 litre of fuel/km
Heavy truck	9.5	1.19
Medium truck	8.0	1.36
Light truck	5.6	2.01
Bus	5.5	1.90
Minibus	3.7	2.89
Land Rover type	2.2	5.10
Large car	1.8	6.12
Small car	0.8	14.10

Table 9.2

Vehicle	$C_D \times S/m^2$	Distance travelled on 1 litre of fuel/km
Heavy truck	4.5	
Bus	3.3	
Light truck	3.1	
Land Rover type	1.4	
Small car	0.5	

Table 9.3

Car	C_D	Frontal area S/m^2
A	0.48	0.8
B	0.45	1.0
C	0.30	2.0

(d) Table 9.3 shows some data for three cars offered for sale at a garage showroom.

The salesperson draws attention to car C's low drag coefficient, saying how much better this car is than either A or B. Criticize the salesperson's comment and discuss which is probably the most economical on fuel.

(Question adapted from one by the author in the Cambridge modular A-level physics specimen paper on transportation and reproduced by permission of the University of Cambridge Local Examinations Syndicate.) ◆

Exploration 9.2   Aerodynamic drag

There are a number of investigations to do with aerodynamic drag that you can choose between.

Part (i) Wind tunnel

Apparatus:

◆ wind tunnel ◆ various model vehicles ◆ cotton

If a wind tunnel is available, investigate how easily air flows past model vehicles at a variety of air speeds. Attach tiny threads of cotton to the outer surface of the models and watch how they line up with the air flow (streamlined) or how they vibrate chaotically (turbulence). Write reports on the models' designs.

Part (ii) Water stream lines

Apparatus:

◆ rectangular glass or plastic sheet (about 45 cm × 30 cm) ◆ rubber gloves
◆ plastic guttering (about 30 cm long) ◆ plastic tube (slightly longer than the guttering and 1 cm diameter) ◆ constant-head apparatus ◆ syringe ◆ water-soluble dye ◆ Plasticine

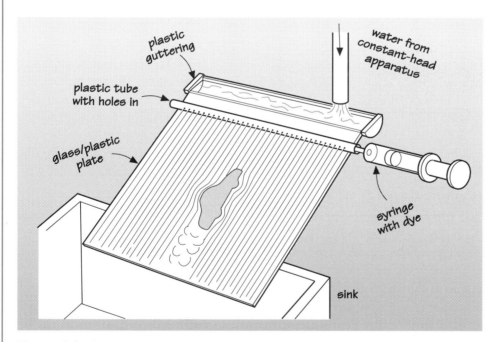

Figure 9.6   Arrangement of equipment for Exploration 9.2(ii)

Attach a plastic or glass sheet just below the rim of a section of slightly tilted plastic guttering that has been closed off at each end. Position the bottom end of the sheet so that it overhangs a sink. Arrange a constant-head apparatus so that the guttering is filled with water at a constant rate and lets the water flow down the sheet. Take a piece of rigid plastic tubing slightly longer than the width of the sheet and seal it at one end.

Make a series of tiny holes, in line with each other and about 0.5 cm apart, along this length of tubing. Position the tubing just above the sheet near its top end with the holes facing downwards. Mould a piece of Plasticine into a two-dimensional cross-sectional sideways view of a vehicle about 1 cm thick. Attach this firmly to the sheet facing upwards. Mix up a strongly coloured dye (wear rubber gloves) and draw this into the syringe. Now attach the syringe to the tubing and push the plunger in, allowing the dye to flow steadily out of the holes on to the plate. Note how the dye lines flow around the model. A change of speed can be modelled by tilting the plate at a steeper angle. Try different shapes of model and report on their characteristics.

Make sure that all the equipment is secured safely and be especially careful when handling the glass sheet.

Part (iii) Computer simulation

Apparatus:

◆ Acorn BBC microcomputer ◆ *Vehicle Designer* software

50-60 MINUTES

If you still have access to an Acorn BBC microcomputer and have a piece of software called *Vehicle Designer*, developed for Heinemann Educational Books by Five Ways Software, then you could report on the performance of the various vehicle shapes provided, together with those of your own design. This piece of software is a very poor relation of the packages used by the Ford Motor Company and its predictions may not always be very realistic. However, it takes up very little computer memory, it is fun to use and it gives you some insight into computer-aided design. Do read the manuals that go with the package before using it. Some print-outs of flow lines, pressure maps and simulated road test data are shown in Figure 9.7 for one of the shapes provided (AERO1).

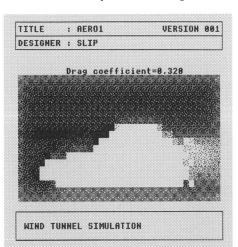

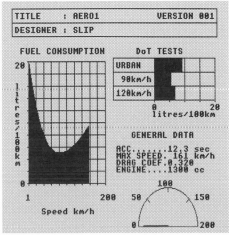

Figure 9.7
Print-outs for AERO1

141

Trains

Compared with cars, trains are a very efficient means of transporting large numbers of people over long distances. Even so, railway engineers are trying both to increase the speed of trains and to decrease the energy per passenger required to move them.

 How can trains be more efficient than cars at transporting large numbers of people over long distances?

One major way is that trains have a relatively low air resistance as each carriage follows directly behind the one before it, effectively **slipstreaming**, which would be dangerous in cars. Railway tracks are designed and engineered to avoid steep gradients and sharp turns to reduce unnecessary energy transfer through braking. Tracks are smooth and so solid wheels can be used, which avoids the energy transfer that causes a pneumatic tyre to warm up because of its continued flexing. You may well be able to think of others.

> The effects of air resistance can easily be illustrated by considering world speed records. With slipstreaming the world record on a bicycle is 68.08 m s^{-1} (245.08 km h^{-1} or 152.28 mph), but without slipstreaming the record for any human powered vehicle is 29.27 m s^{-1} (105.36 km h^{-1} or 65.48 mph).

Q4 Vehicles travelling at speed v have to overcome frictional forces of resistance resulting in a net force called drag, given by the formula

$$\text{drag force} = A + Bv + Cv^2$$

where A, B and C are drag factors. Thus, at a steady speed, the power developed by the engine is used to do work against these forces.

The data in Table 9.4 were obtained in trials of various kinds of passenger trains, including an experimental Advanced Passenger Train (APT).

Table 9.4

Train type	Drag factors		
	A/N	$B/\text{N m}^{-1}\text{s}$	$C/\text{N m}^{-2}\text{s}^2$
APT7730	123	8.67	
Class 87 + 10 MkIIF coaches	6601	40.0	18.45
High-speed train + 7 coaches	2650	69.0	10.37

The mass, m, of the vehicle is also important. Transfer of energy is required to accelerate a train from rest, the kinetic energy transferred being given by the formula

$$\text{kinetic energy} = \frac{1}{2}mv^2$$

The mass affects gravitational potential energy transfer too. When the train is climbing a gradient, a transfer of **chemical potential energy** from the diesel fuel to **gravitational potential energy** takes place. The change in gravitational potential energy is given by

$$\text{potential energy} = mgh$$

where h is the vertical height risen. Unlike energy transferred to overcome drag, both kinetic and potential energy are, in theory, recoverable.

(a) Calculate the drag force when each train is travelling at a speed of 44.0 m s^{-1}: (i) the APT, (ii) the class 87 train + 10 coaches, (iii) the high-speed train + 7 coaches.

(b) Without doing any detailed calculations, explain why it is reasonable to expect that the design of the APT is more effective at high speeds than at low speeds.

(c) The APT has mass 4.2×10^5 kg. Calculate: (i) its kinetic energy when it is travelling at a speed of 44 m s^{-1}, (ii) the work done per second by the engine at this speed.

(d) Explain why, unlike energy transferred to overcome drag, both kinetic and potential energy are recoverable.

(e) Describe briefly a way in which engineers could arrange the design of the train so that kinetic energy could, in practice, be recovered.

(Question adapted from one in the Cambridge modular A-level physics specimen foundation paper and reproduced by permission of the University of Cambridge Local Examinations Syndicate.) ◆

Q5 Computer print-outs for designs called WEDGE1 and WEDGE2 are shown in Figures 9.8 and 9.9. Comment on the performance of these designs compared with AERO1. ◆

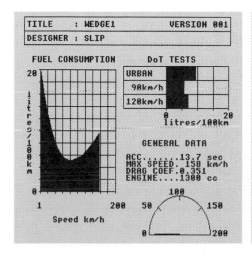
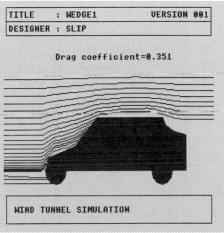

Figure 9.8
Print-outs for
WEDGE1

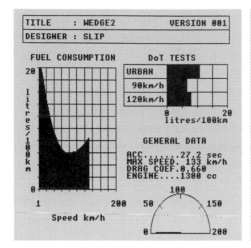

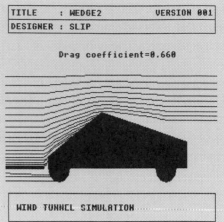

Figure 9.9
Print-outs for
WEDGE2

 Exploration 9.3 Investigating car kits

As you will have noticed, all cars today are designed to reduce aerodynamic drag as much as possible. Some companies do, however, produce kits that are intended to reduce this drag still further. The following problem is about whether or not to recommend to your employers the fitting of any of the following kits to its fleet of cars. If you tackle this you will need to write a report, backed up by explanatory data, detailing the merits (if any) of particular kits and whether they are likely to be a worthwhile investment. The data has been taken from the article 'Raising the wind' by Jeff Daniels, which appeared in *Performance Car* magazine in April 1984. Our answer to the problem is given after the answers to the questions at the end of this section.

Tables 9.5–9.7 show how the aerodynamic drag force, front **lift force** and rear lift force vary with the **yaw angle** on a standard (unaltered) XR3i Ford Escort and on the same model fitted with the Cartel, Kamei, KAT I and KAT II kits.

Hints for writing your report

First you must agree with your teacher and fellow students what form the report is to take. A full written report needs a paragraph or two to explain and define technical terms, e.g. front lift force, drag, yaw. In another paragraph you would need to describe the effects of all the forces on performance from a physicist's point of view.

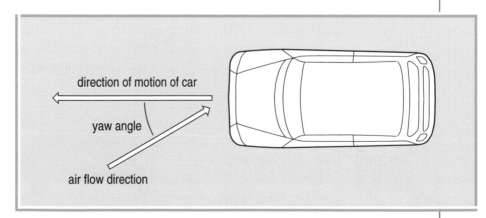

Figure 9.10 Yaw angle

144

Table 9.5 Drag force

Model	Drag force at 60 mph/N		
	Yaw angle 0°	Yaw angle 10°	Yaw angle 20°
Standard	322.9	336.7	373.2
Cartel	332.7	356.7	390.5
Kamei	319.4	350.9	395.9
KAT I	310.0	351.4	394.4
KAT II	310.5	354.1	393.6

Figure 9.10 shows the meaning of yaw angle. Cars frequently move about with yaw angles of 20° or more.

We are also interested in keeping the car's tyres in good contact with the road. To do this front and rear lift forces must be as low as possible. Tables 9.6 and 9.7 provide values of the front and rear lift forces for various yaw angles.

Table 9.6 Front lift force

Model	Front lift force at 60 mph/N		
	Yaw angle 0°	Yaw angle 10°	Yaw angle 20°
Standard	118.3	189.5	294.0
Cartel	104.1	155.2	213.1
Kamei	97.0	148.1	214.4
KAT I	88.5	136.6	238.0
KAT II	82.7	132.1	238.0

Table 9.7 Rear lift force

Model	Rear lift force at 60 mph/N		
	Yaw angle 0°	Yaw angle 10°	Yaw angle 20°
Standard	28.5	55.6	171.7
Cartel	54.3	91.6	127.2
Kamei	93.9	99.2	159.2
KAT I	117.4	130.8	196.6
KAT II	76.5	99.2	167.7

9.3 Safety with fuels

The safety of vehicles is not just about crash protection and controlled braking. There are major dangers of another kind when large quantities of fuel are transferred at speed along pipelines and when they are filtered.

 Why do you suppose high fuel transfer rates are needed when refuelling large international airliners?

International airliners are very expensive to operate. The more often they can fly, the more economically they can be operated. Speeding up refuelling will provide more time for flying.

 Why is efficient filtering of the fuel required?

Any dirt in the fuel could be very dangerous – it could cause a blockage to the engine and so cut off the power.

So what is the nature of the problem? Where the fuel makes contact with the wall of the pipeline, a corner or a filter, turbulence (a churning up of the fuel) tends to occur and this often ionizes the fuel. Enough energy is transferred from the moving fuel to knock **electrons** off the hydrocarbon molecules – to **ionize** them. This is made worse by the fact that fuels usually contain small amounts of water. Water is far easier to ionize than the hydrocarbon molecules.

The electrons, freed from the atoms and molecules, tend to migrate to the walls of the pipe and the now positively charged fuel continues along the pipeline into the fuel tank. This in turn results in large charge differences between the pipeline and the fuel tank and so large potential differences between them too. If the latter are large enough to produce a spark then there is an obvious problem.

 STADIS 450, a highly conductive fuel additive, is usually added to aviation fuels. Explain how you think this reduces the charge build up.

By making the fuel more conductive it allows the separated charges to recombine more quickly and so produce a neutral, uncharged, fuel.

As you might guess, the key variables involved in how much charge is generated are

■ the speed of flow of the fuel
■ the **conductivity** of the fuel
■ the amount of turbulence produced.

You can investigate these in Exploration 9.4.

Experimental work will probably have to be arranged with the advice and supervision of your teacher. If you have to wait a day or two, you can still go on with your study; skip to the next section – 'A little theory first'.

Exploration 9.4   Charge generation in fuels

Apparatus:

◆ electrometer ◆ copper pipe ◆ pan scourer ◆ rubber hose
◆ electric leads ◆ funnel ◆ measuring jug ◆ PVC insulating
tiles ◆ metal can ◆ paraffin ◆ water

Set up and secure safely the equipment as shown in Figure 9.11.

Your task is to investigate, and report on, the effect on the charge separation created of (i) speed of flow, (ii) change in the paraffin/water ratio and (iii) degree of turbulence produced by filtration.

A pan scourer, metal or plastic, should make quite a good filter. To produce noticeable effects add just a few millilitres of paraffin to each litre of water. This may not appear to be very realistic 'fuel' but you will be trying to model a process that takes place at much higher flow rates and with very large volumes. You could also try water alone.

Use a paraffin/water mixture to lessen the fire hazard.
Do not use petrol or aviation spirit.
Wear rubber gloves when handling the liquids.
Use a small dropper bottle of paraffin and replace the stopper when not in use.
Do not work near naked flames.
Keep room well ventilated to avoid the risk of fire.

100-120 MINUTES

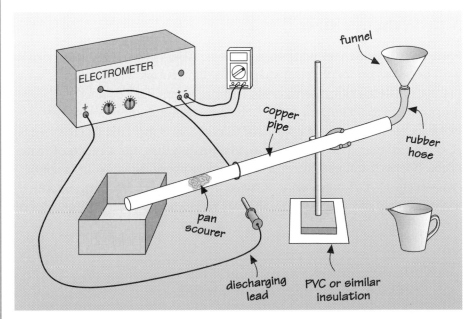

Figure 9.11
Arrangement of the apparatus

One measure of the amount of ionization that has taken place will be the fuel/water mixture's conductivity. The more ions there are in it, the more conductive it will have become. In your earlier science course you will have measured the **resistance** of a device – an electrical resistor, a light bulb, a piece of wire, or perhaps a light dependent resistor (LDR). You will have set up the circuit shown in Figure 9.12. Discharge the pipe between experiments by connecting the discharging lead (connected to Earth) to it. Stand back from the apparatus as you take readings – you may be charged up too if you are too close.

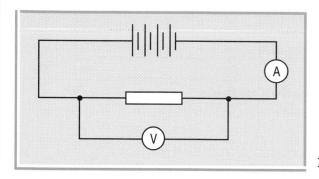

Figure 9.12 Circuit to measure resistance

To calculate the specimen's resistance you will have recorded the current, I, flowing through it and the potential difference or voltage, V, across it. Its resistance, R, is then given by $R = V/I$. However, this is a property of the specimen and not of the material from which it is made. We need to find the material's **resistivity** or conductivity. You might be able to do this for the paraffin/water mixture if you have access to an electrometer, a d.c. amplifier, a picoammeter or a conductivity meter of sufficient sensitivity. The following section shows how you might go about this.

A little theory first

From earlier work you will probably remember how the resistance of a wire depends on its physical shape and dimensions. For example, for a piece of material of uniform cross-section, its resistance, R, is proportional to its length, L. If it is twice as long, then its resistance is twice as great. The other important dimension is the area of cross-section, A, of the sample. This leads to the relationship that, for a piece of material of fixed length, its resistance, R, is inversely proportional to its area of cross-section, A. If it is a wire of twice the original radius, and so four times the area of cross-section, then its resistance will be one-quarter of the original.

So

$$R \propto L$$

and

$$R \propto \frac{1}{A}$$

You may find the relationship between area of cross-section and resistance harder to accept than the relationship with length if this is the first time you have thought about it. Combining these together we have

$$R = \rho \frac{L}{A} \qquad (9.2)$$

where ρ is the constant of proportionality known as the material's resistivity, or alternatively

$$R = \frac{L}{\sigma A} \qquad (9.3)$$

where σ (sigma) is the constant of proportionality known as the material's conductivity.

 What are the units of measurement for resistivity and for conductivity?

Re-arrange Equations (9.2) and (9.3) to get

$$\rho = \frac{R \text{ (ohms) } A \text{ (metres}^2)}{L \text{ (metres)}}$$

$$\sigma = \frac{L \text{ (metres)}}{A \text{ (metres}^2) \ R \text{ (ohms)}}$$

This gives units of resistivity as Ω m (ohm metre), and of conductivity as Ω^{-1} m^{-1} (ohm^{-1} metre^{-1}). The units of conductivity are also often given as S m^{-1} (siemens per metre).

 What effect will having a high resistivity have on the resistance of a piece of material of fixed length and area of cross-section?

It will make it have a high resistance.

 What effect will having a high conductivity have on the resistance of a piece of material of fixed length and area of cross-section?

It will make it have a low resistance.

The siemens is the unit of **conductance**. Conductance is the reciprocal of resistance and is given the symbol G.

How does the equation to define resistance $R = \dfrac{V}{I}$ appear when the conductance is used rather than resistance?

Since

$$G = \frac{1}{R}$$

then

$$G = \frac{I}{V} \tag{9.4}$$

Exploration 9.5 will give you practical experience of using Equations (9.2), (9.3) and (9.4). It is important that you fully understand the physical quantities involved.

 Exploration 9.5   Measuring the resistivity and conductivity of conducting putty

Apparatus:

◆ battery or low-voltage power supply ◆ ammeter ◆ voltmeter
◆ two metal plate electrodes ◆ electric leads ◆ conducting putty
◆ plastic gloves

Use the plastic gloves when handling the conducting putty.

Wearing plastic gloves, mould a piece of conducting putty (Unilab 111.120) into a shape whose length and area of cross-section are easy to measure. Place electrodes, with leads attached to them, at the ends of the specimen you have moulded. Connect these into the circuit shown in Figure 9.13.

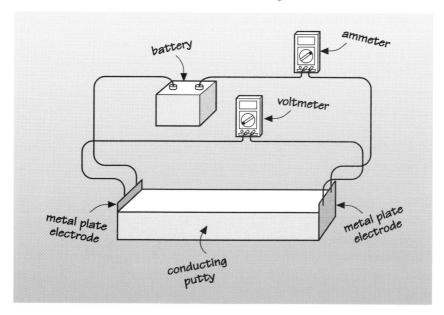

Figure 9.13
Circuit arrangement for measuring resistivity and conductivity

Record

(i) the current, I, in amperes that is flowing

(ii) the voltage or potential difference, V, in volts across the specimen

(iii) the specimen's area of cross-section, A, in square metres

(iv) the specimen's length, L, in metres.

Use the data recorded to calculate the resistivity and conductivity of the conducting putty. Repeat with half the length of the specimen and show that the resistivity and conductivity are virtually unchanged, being properties of the material and not of the specimen.

As a follow-up to Exploration 9.4 on the charging up of the paraffin/water mixture, you could, if you have sensitive enough equipment, now look at how these mixtures change in conductivity with changes in their mixture ratio, flow rates, induced turbulence, etc., and report on these. Charged up fluids are usually left in settling tanks for some time to allow discharge to Earth and recombination of separated out charges. You could also examine this.

Write a report on this exploration and discuss it with other students and your teacher.

In the following questions you will have an opportunity to apply the ideas you have developed from your explorations and theory.

Q6 (a) Imagine a liquid cube of highly purified hydrocarbon fuel. If the dimensions of the cube are 0.05 m × 0.05 m × 0.05 m and the liquid's conductivity is 10^{-15} S m^{-1}, what would be the resistance across opposite faces of this cube?

(b) To measure the resistance across this cube a student sets up the circuit shown in Figure 9.14 with the fuel being contained in a vessel of zero conductivity and of internal dimensions 0.05 m × 0.05 m × 0.05 m.

Two opposite walls of the container are coated with a very thin layer of silver to make them into conducting electrodes. What current would you expect the ammeter to indicate? Comment on the feasibility of measuring this.

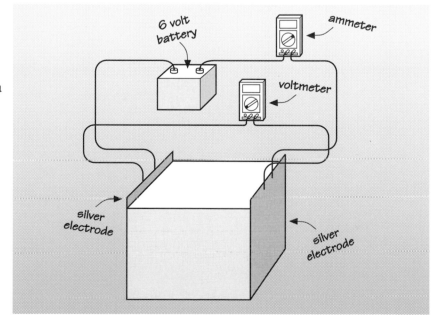

Figure 9.14
Measuring current flowing in circuit

(c) Zero conductivity is very difficult to obtain – a perfect vacuum is needed. What problems would a glass container cause if the effect of it is to place a resistance of 2×10^{15} Ω between the two electrodes? Explain your answer.

(d) To measure the resistance, R_{fuel}, of the fuel between the two electrodes this same student wishes also to record the potential difference, V, between the electrodes. R_{fuel} will then be calculated from

$$R_{fuel} = \frac{V}{I}$$

where I was the current flowing between the two electrodes. Most ordinary voltmeters have a resistance of around 10 MΩ (10 megohms or 10 000 000 ohms). How sensible would it have been to measure such a voltage with this type of meter? Explain your answer. ◆

Q7   In transferring fuel to a road tanker the relationship between the highest safe loading velocity, v (in metres per second), the pipeline diameter, d (in metres), and the product's conductivity, σ (in pS m^{-1}, i.e. picosiemens per metre – pico means 10^{-12}), is:

$$v^2 d^2 = c\sigma$$

where c is a constant with a value of approximately 0.1 m^5 s^{-2} pS^{-1}.

(a) If the conductivity of a fuel is 0.8 pS m^{-1} and the pipeline diameter is 0.1 m, calculate the highest safe loading velocity.

(b) If a small quantity of a fuel additive called STADIS 450 is put into this fuel its conductivity rises to 200 pS m^{-1}. At what speed could this fuel now be safely loaded? ◆

Achievements

After working through this section you should be able to:

- apply a simple theory of drag forces
- calculate energy transfers
- calculate the efficiency of energy transfers
- describe the dangers of moving fuels around due to turbulence
- define resistance and conductance (and understand that one is the inverse of the other) and give their units
- define resistivity and conductivity of materials and give their units
- derive and use the equation for resistivity

$$R = \frac{\rho L}{A}$$

- use the equation for conductivity

$$R = \frac{L}{\sigma A}$$

- carry out data analyses
- use, and understand the use of, an electrometer, a d.c. amplifier, a coulomb meter, a picoammeter and a conductivity meter
- obtain practical experiences of some or all of the following:
  - fluid brake design
  - some ways to affect the drag forces in water or air
  - charge separation in fuels
  - measuring the resistivity of a material.

Glossary

Chemical potential energy The energy that is stored within the structure of chemicals.

Conductance Unit: siemens (S). An electrical quantity, G, that is the reciprocal of *resistance* and is defined by the expression $G = \frac{I}{V}$, where I is the current flowing through the device and V is the potential difference or voltage across it.

Conductivity Units: siemens per metre (S m^{-1}). An electrical quantity, σ, which is defined by the expression $\sigma = \frac{L}{RA}$, where L is the length of the sample, R is its resistance and A is its cross-sectional area. Conductivity is the reciprocal of resistivity.

Drag When an object and fluid move relative to each other a drag (force) is experienced in the opposite direction to the motion. Vehicles today are designed to reduce this drag and so have as small a drag coefficient (C_D) and frontal area as is practicable. Drag, being a force, is measured in newtons (N) and is a vector quantity. The drag coefficient will be affected by the direction of travel of the vehicle.

Electron A tiny particle having a negative charge of approximately 1.6×10^{-19} C. It was discovered in 1897 by Sir Joseph John Thomson.

Fluid brake *See hydrokinetic brake.*

Gravitational potential energy The energy that is associated with the height of an object, or more accurately with its position within a gravitational field. The energy that is transferred to or from an object as it moves up and down close to the Earth is given by PE = mgh.

Hydrokinetic brake A braking mechanism in which fluids, impacting on surfaces, cause braking forces because of the change of momentum produced. They are also known as fluid brakes.

Ion An electrically charged atom or molecule.

Ionize Formation of ions, usually by gaining or losing electrons.

Lift force   Unit: newton (N). The effect of moving a fluid over a surface can result in a lift force being exerted on it. The best known result of this is the lift attained by an aeroplane. Cars also experience lift, particularly at high speeds, and aerofoil 'wings' are put on racing cars and dragsters to produce an opposite effect to lift. Lift force is a vector quantity.

Resistance   .Unit: ohm (Ω). An electrical quantity, R, which is defined by the expression $R = \dfrac{V}{I}$, where V is the potential difference or voltage across the device and I is the current flowing through it.

Resistivity   Unit: ohm metre (Ω m). An electrical quantity defined by the expression $\sigma = \dfrac{RA}{L}$, where R is the *resistance* of a sample of length L and cross-sectional area A.

Slipstreaming   Attempting to avoid the effects of air resistance on a moving object by arranging for it to follow closely behind another object moving at the same speed.

Streamlining   Flow is said to be streamlined if it is steady and has successive particles in the fluid passing a fixed point travelling at the same velocity. Flow of this nature will minimize drag.

Turbulence   Flow is said to be turbulent if the velocity of successive particles in the fluid passing a fixed point varies with time. This infers a churning up of the fluid. Flow of this nature will increase drag.

Yaw angle   The angle between the direction of motion of a vehicle and the fluid (usually air) through which it moves. It is measured in degrees.

Answers to Ready to Study test

R1

(a) The diagram should be similar to Figure 9.15.

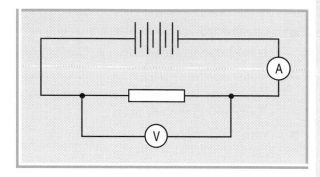

Figure 9.15

(b)

$$R = \frac{V}{I}$$

$$\text{resistance} = \frac{\text{potential difference across wire}}{\text{current through wire}}$$

potential difference is measured in volts

current is measured in amperes

resistance is measured in ohms.

R2

(a) Atoms contain electrons (with negative charge) orbiting a nucleus of protons (positive charge) and neutrons (no charge).

(b) Most currents flow along metal conductors where the principal carrier will be electrons. Electrons are not the only charged particles that move. Any movement of charged particles will produce the effects we recognize as those of electrical currents (e.g. heating up of wires, production of magnetic fields).

(c) Ionization occurs when electrically neutral atoms or molecules gain or lose one or more electrons. The resulting nucleus plus electrons is called an **ion**. Ionization may also result in free moving electrons (with a negative charge).

R3

(a) 0.01 Ω. The resistance is halved.

(b) 0.005 Ω. This wire has twice the cross-sectional area and therefore half the resistance of each separate piece.

R4

The effect is to decrease the effective resistance of the circuit. The current measured would be increased, which gives a lower value for the resistance, R.

R5

Power = force × velocity

The units are as follows:
power – W or J s^{-1}
force – N
velocity – m s^{-1}.

Taking the right-hand side of the expression, force (N) × velocity (m s^{-1}) gives N m s^{-1}. A newton metre is also a joule, so we now have J s^{-1}, which is the unit of power.

R6

volume = base × height
$\qquad$ = A × distance travelled

We know that distance travelled is vt from the equation

$$v = \frac{s}{t}$$

so

volume = $A \times vt$
$\qquad$ = Avt

R7

(a)

$$\text{Density} = \frac{\text{mass}}{\text{volume}}$$

so

$$\text{volume} = \frac{\text{mass}}{\text{density}}$$

$$= \frac{680\,000\,\text{kg}}{13\,600\,\text{kg}\,\text{m}^{-3}}$$

$$= 50\,\text{m}^3$$

(b)

$$\text{Density} = \frac{\text{mass}}{\text{volume}}$$

so

mass = density × volume

$$= 13\,600\,\text{kg}\,\text{m}^{-3} \times 2.5\,\text{m}^3$$

$$= 34\,000\,\text{kg}$$

$$= 3.4 \times 10^4 \text{ kg (to two significant figures)}$$

(c)

Energy transferred

$$= \text{mass} \times \text{specific heat capacity}$$
$$\times \text{temperature change}$$

$$= 1.5\,\text{kg} \times 139\,\text{J}\,\text{kg}^{-1}\,\text{K}^{-1} \times 3\,\text{K}$$

$$= 625.5\,\text{J}$$

$$= 6 \times 10^2 \text{ J}$$

$$\text{(to one significant figure)}$$

Answers to questions in the text

Q1

(a)

Gravitational potential energy transferred

$$= mg\Delta h$$

where $m = 1$ kg, $g = 10$ N kg^{-1} and $\Delta h - 100$ m.

Giving

Gravitational potential energy transferred

$$= 1\,\text{kg} \times 10\,\text{N}\,\text{kg}^{-1} \times 100\,\text{m}$$

$$= 1000\,\text{J}$$

$$= 1 \times 10^3\,\text{J}$$

(to one significant figure)

(b)

Energy transferred in heating $= m \times s \times \Delta\theta$

where $m = 1$ kg, $s = 4200$ J kg^{-1} K^{-1} and $\Delta\theta$ is the temperature rise.

Giving

energy transferred in heating

$$= 1\,\text{kg} \times 4200\,\text{J}\,\text{kg}^{-1}\,\text{K}^{-1} \times \Delta\theta$$

$$= 1000\,\text{J}$$

so

$$\Delta\theta = \frac{1000\,\text{J}}{\left(1\,\text{kg} \times 4200\,\text{J}\,\text{kg}^{-1}\,\text{K}^{-1}\right)}$$

$$= 0.238\,\text{K}$$

$$= 0.2\,\text{K (to one significant figure)}$$

(c)

Energy transferred in heating $= m \times s \times \Delta\theta$

where $m = 1$ kg, $s = 4200$ J kg^{-1} K^{-1}, $\Delta\theta = 0.04$ K.

Giving

energy transferred in heating

$$= 1\,\text{kg} \times 4200\,\text{J}\,\text{kg}^{-1}\,\text{K}^{-1} \times 0.04\,\text{K}$$

$$= 168\,\text{J}$$

$$= 2 \times 10^2\,\text{J}$$

(to one significant figure)

(d) Efficiency is then given by

$$\frac{168\,\text{J}}{1000\,\text{J}} \times 100\% = 16.8\%$$

$$= 2 \times 10^1\%$$

(to one significant figure)

(e) Some to the air with which it collided on the way to the foot of the waterfall, some to the rest of the water, some to the rock base of the waterfall and some to the air at the foot of the waterfall. Some might also go to raise water droplets as they bounce from the water's surface.

Q2

(a) (i)

Aerodynamic drag force

$$= \frac{1}{2}\left[1.2\,\text{kg}\,\text{m}^{-3} \times 2\,\text{m}^2 \times \left(10\,\text{m}\,\text{s}^{-1}\right)^2 \times 0.34\right]$$

$$= 40.8\,\text{N}$$

$$= 41\,\text{N (to two significant figures)}$$

(ii)

Aerodynamic drag force

$$= \frac{1}{2}\left[1.2\,\text{kg}\,\text{m}^{-3} \times 2\,\text{m}^2 \times \left(20\,\text{m}\,\text{s}^{-1}\right)^2 \times 0.34\right]$$

$$= 163.2\,\text{N}$$

$$= 1.6 \times 10^2\,\text{N (to two significant figures)}$$

(iii)

Aerodynamic drag force

$$= \frac{1}{2}\left[1.2\,\text{kg}\,\text{m}^{-3} \times 2\,\text{m}^2 \times \left(30\,\text{ms}^{-1}\right)^2 \times 0.34\right]$$

$$= 367.2\,\text{N}$$

$$= 3.7 \times 10^2 \text{ N (to two significant figures)}$$

(iv)

Aerodynamic drag force

$$= \frac{1}{2}\left[1.2\,\text{kg}\,\text{m}^{-3} \times 2\,\text{m}^2 \times \left(40\,\text{ms}^{-1}\right)^2 \times 0.34\right]$$

$$= 652.8\,\text{N}$$

$$= 6.5 \times 10^2 \text{ N (to two significant figures)}$$

(b)

Work done against drag
$$= \text{drag force} \times \text{distance travelled}$$

Power to overcome drag

$$= \frac{\text{work done against drag}}{\text{time taken}}$$

$$= \frac{\text{drag force} \times \text{distance travelled}}{\text{time taken}}$$

$$= \text{drag force} \times \frac{\text{distance travelled}}{\text{time taken}}$$

$$= \text{drag force} \times \text{velocity of the vehicle}$$

(c) (i)

Power to overcome drag $= 40.8\,\text{N} \times 10\,\text{ms}^{-1}$

$$= 408\,\text{W}$$

(ii)

Power to overcome drag $= 163.2\,\text{N} \times 20\,\text{ms}^{-1}$

$$= 3264\,\text{W}$$

(iii)

Power to overcome drag $= 367.2\,\text{N} \times 30\,\text{ms}^{-1}$

$$= 11016\,\text{W}$$

(iv)

Power to overcome drag $= 652.8\,\text{N} \times 40\,\text{ms}^{-1}$

$$= 26112\,\text{W}$$

(d) Maximum power output = total opposing forces × maximum vehicle velocity

giving

60 000 W = 1200 N
× maximum vehicle velocity

so

$$\text{maximum vehicle velocity} = \frac{60\,000\,\text{W}}{1200\,\text{N}}$$

$$= 50\,\text{ms}^{-1}$$

Q3

(a) If you have put $(C_D \times S)$ on the y-axis and distance on the x-axis you should have a curve that starts high on the left, drops fairly steeply at first, then becomes more shallow and ends up low on the right.

(b) $(C_D \times S)$ is inversely proportional to distance travelled on 1 litre of fuel.

(c) (i) Taking the first four values from our graph we have: 2.47, 3.33, 3.55 and 8.0. As the final value is beyond the curve we have drawn we can work it out as follows. The product of the two adjacent columns should give approximately the same value. Taking the first pair we have (4.5 × 2.5) which gives 11.25, or about 11. So the last pairing $(0.5 \times x) \approx 11$, giving x a value of about 22.5 km.

As the values are taken from a graph plot you may find that your answers are slightly different from ours.

(ii) The final value for the small car relies on the relationship still holding beyond the measurements that have been made. This requires extrapolation, so it is not a very reliable value.

(d) The important factor is $(C_D \times S)$ and this is highest for car C. The most economical car is likely to be A, for which this factor is 0.38 – the lowest of the three.

Q4

(a)

Drag force $= A + Bv + Cv^2$

(i)

$$\text{Drag force} = 7730\,\text{N} + \left(123\,\text{N}\,\text{m}^{-1}\,\text{s} \times 44.0\,\text{m}\,\text{s}^{-1}\right)$$
$$+ \left(8.67\,\text{N}\,\text{m}^{-2}\,\text{s}^2 \times 44.0^2\,\text{m}^2\,\text{s}^{-2}\right)$$
$$= 29\,927.12\,\text{N}$$

(ii)

$$\text{Drag force} = 6601\,\text{N} + \left(40.0\,\text{N}\,\text{m}^{-1}\,\text{s} \times 44.0\,\text{m}\,\text{s}^{-1}\right)$$
$$+ \left(18.45\,\text{N}\,\text{m}^{-2}\,\text{s}^2 \times 44.0^2\,\text{m}^2\,\text{s}^{-2}\right)$$
$$= 44\,080.2\,\text{N}$$

(iii)

$$\text{Drag force} = 2650\,\text{N} + \left(69.0\,\text{N}\,\text{m}^{-1}\,\text{s} \times 44.0\,\text{m}\,\text{s}^{-1}\right)$$
$$+ \left(10.37\,\text{N}\,\text{m}^{-2}\,\text{s}^2 \times 44.0^2\,\text{m}^2\,\text{s}^{-2}\right)$$
$$= 25\,762.32\,\text{N}$$

(b) The drag factor C, which is multiplied by the square of the train's speed, is small, hence this otherwise large product is kept small.

(c) (i)

$$\text{Kinetic energy} = \frac{1}{2} \times m \times v^2$$
$$= \frac{1}{2}\left[4.20 \times 10^5\,\text{kg} \times \left(44\,\text{m}\,\text{s}^{-1}\right)^2\right]$$
$$= 4.0656 \times 10^8\,\text{J}$$
$$= 4.1 \times 10^8\,\text{J}$$

(to two significant figures)

(ii)

Work done per second by the engine

$$= \text{total drag force} \times \text{speed of train}$$
$$= 29\,927.12\,\text{N} \times 44\,\text{m}\,\text{s}^{-1}$$
$$= 1316\,793.3\,\text{W}$$
$$= 1.3\,\text{MW (to two significant figures)}$$

(d) The energy transferred in overcoming drag will be heating the surrounding atmosphere and so will not be recoverable. Kinetic and potential energy can be transferred without always heating things up and so are recoverable.

(e) The train could be designed so that, in braking, the electric motors could act as a dynamo and transfer the train's kinetic energy back into the electricity supply system.

Q5

The fuel consumptions of WEDGE1 and AERO1 are very similar, though in each test WEDGE1 is slightly worse. WEDGE1 also has a slightly poorer acceleration time and maximum speed. These would be consistent with a slightly higher drag coefficient. WEDGE2 has poorer fuel consumption figures, a longer acceleration time and lower maximum speed – all consistent with its higher drag coefficient. With WEDGE2, the air flow over the car body does not appear as smooth as that of the other two models.

Q6

(a)

$$R = \frac{L}{\sigma A}$$
$$= \frac{0.05\,\text{m}}{10^{-15}\,\text{S}\,\text{m}^{-1} \times (0.05 \times 0.05)\,\text{m}^2}$$
$$= 2.0 \times 10^{16}\,\Omega$$

(b)

$$I = \frac{V}{R}$$

$$= \frac{6\,\mathrm{V}}{2\times10^{16}\,\Omega}$$

$$= 3\times10^{-16}\,\mathrm{A}$$

This is very tiny indeed and probably beyond the capability of school instrumentation!

(c) Most of the current would flow through the glass container, it effectively being in parallel with the fuel and of lower resistance, and so the measurements obtained would be highly misleading.

(d) It would not be at all sensible, for almost all the current will now be flowing through the voltmeter rather than through the fuel. The resistance recorded would be that of the meter and not of the fuel.

Q7

(a) Since
$$v^2 d^2 = c\sigma$$

we now have

$$v^2 \times (0.1\ \mathrm{m})^2 = 0.1\,\mathrm{m}^5\,\mathrm{s}^{-2}\,\mathrm{pS}^{-1}\times0.8\,\mathrm{pS\,m}^{-1}$$

so

$$v^2 = \frac{(0.1\times0.8)\,\mathrm{m}^4\,\mathrm{s}^{-2}}{(0.1\mathrm{m})^2}$$

$$= 8\,\mathrm{m}^2\,\mathrm{s}^{-2}$$

Hence the highest safe loading velocity is $\sqrt{8}\,\mathrm{m\,s}^{-1}$ or 2.83 m s^{-1}.

(b) Using the same expression we have

$$v^2 \times (0.1\ \mathrm{m})^2 = 0.1\times200\ \mathrm{pS\ m}^{-1}$$

so

$$v^2 = \frac{0.1\times200\,\mathrm{pS\,m}^{-1}}{(0.1\mathrm{m})^2}$$

$$= 2000\,\mathrm{m}^2\,\mathrm{s}^{-2}$$

Hence the highest safe loading velocity is now $\sqrt{2000}\,\mathrm{m\,s}^{-1}$ or 44.72 m s^{-1}.

Answer to Exploration 9.3

As you can see from Table 9.5, whilst the drag force is reduced by Kamei, KAT I and KAT II kits at 0° yaw, the drag is increased for all kits at yaw angles of 10° and 20°. As vehicles are often driven with yaw angles greater than zero, this means that adding any of the kits would make the vehicle use more fuel than the standard model. Looking at Table 9.6, the kits have an advantage at all yaw angles in lessening the front lift force. However, you can see from Table 9.7 that the only advantages for rear lift force are offered by the Cartel and KAT II kits at a yaw angle of 20°; all the other results indicate poorer performance than the standard model. Overall it appears that the standard model gives the best all-round performance when all three factors are taken into consideration.

If you think back to the beginning of this unit, you will realize what a long way you have come – from your first exploration, which involved finding the centre of gravity of a tractor, through considering human safety in crashes, to an analysis of the aerodynamics of some car body kits.

To help you to appreciate how far you have come, look back through the list of achievements for each section. If you feel unsure about any of them, go over the relevant section(s) of this unit again. When you feel fairly confident about most of these achievements ask your teacher for the exit test for this unit. When you have done the test, consult your teacher, who has the answers and will probably wish to go through them with you. We hope you have enjoyed learning about the physics of movement with this supported learning unit, and that you want to use more units in the series.

CONCLUSION

Further reading and resources

AA Magazines. In particular: 'Crash barriers' (no. 10, autumn 1994); 'An airbag saved my life' (no. 11, winter 1995). AA Magazines, Norfolk House, Priestly Road, Basingstoke, Hants RG24 9NY,

Allen, J. E. (1986) *Aerodynamics – the science of air in motion.* Allen Brothers and Father, Blythburgh. The definitive text on this subject.

Atkinson, J. K. (1989) *Transducers.* NEMEC, University of Southampton.

Baker, A. K. (1986) *Vehicle Braking.* Pentech Press, London. This gives comprehensive details of braking in vehicles.

Bannister, B. R. and Whitehead, D. G. (1986) *Transducers and Interfacing – principles and techniques.* Van Nostrand, Wokingham.

Bishop, O. N. (1991) *Practical Electronic Sensors.* Bernard Babani, London. This gives full details of the physics of various sensors and how they can be interfaced.

Bright, A. W., Corbett, R. P. and Hughes, J. F. (1978) *Electrostatics,* no. 30 of series *Engineering and Design Guide.* Oxford University Press, Oxford. An excellent insight into applications of electrostatics and its hazards.

Brindley, K. (1988) *Sensors and Transducers.* Heinemann Professional Publishing, Oxford. This has very clear details indeed – an excellent text.

Bryan, G. T. (1970) *Control Systems for Technicians,* 2nd edn. Hodder and Stoughton, Sevenoaks. A good introduction to sensors, control and interfacing.

Complete Car Magazine: 'Driven to destruction', 'Are we being sold a dummy?', 'What's the damage?', 'Secrets under the floorboards' (November 1994); 'Childseat safety in doubt', 'When David and Goliath collide', 'Covered on all sides', 'Crunching the Polo' (April 1995).

Constable, J. (1984) *Aerospace Dynamics,* no. 13. (Technical journal of British Aerospace Dynamics Group, PO Box 600, Six Hills Way, Stevenage, Herts SG1 2DA.)

Curtis, A. (1985) *The Penguin Book of the Car.* Penguin, Harmondsworth. A fairly easy-going text on how a car works.

Farman. J. (1991) *A Suspiciously Simple History of Science and Invention.* Piccadilly Press. London.

Focus Magazine: 'How the twin-tread deals with downpour' (February 1994); 'Why do today's new cars all look alike?' (March 1994); 'The new FDR (road handling) system – getting a grip' (June 1994); 'The low friction tyres that keep a tight grip' (May 1995); 'Smooth your path' (September 1995); 'How it works – the fuel cell' (October 1995); 'How to clean the air – drive!' (October 1995); 'Electric dreams – motor racing with the battery pack' (November 1995); 'Tread carefully' (January 1996); 'When safety kills' (May 1996).

Hannah, J. and Hillier, M. J. (1995) *Applied Mechanics*, 3rd edn. Longman Scientific and Technical, Harlow. An excellent support text on the whole of this topic, together with worked examples and many problems to tackle.

Hillier, V. A. W. (1987) *Fundamentals of Automotive Electronics*. Hutchinson, London. This has a good section on sensors applied to automobiles and how they work.

Hillier, V. A. W. (1991) *Fundamentals of Motor Vehicle Technology*, 4th edn. Hutchinson, Cheltenham. The definitive text in this subject area.

John, R. (ed.) (1994) *The Consumer Revolution: redressing the balance*. Hodder and Stoughton in association with the Consumers' Association, London. Amongst many interesting articles it has one on product testing that is particularly relevant.

Mason, P. I. (1981) 'Electrostatic hazards in liquid transport'. BP Oil International, London, Ref. OS408/81/U. This details the risks and how they are dealt with.

Michelin Tyre plc (1995) *The New Michelin Energy Tyres*. Pamphlet of information on the Michelin Energy Tyres, with science included. Obtainable from Marketing Department, Michelin Tyre plc, The Edward Hyde Building, 38 Clarendon Road, Watford WD1 1SX.

Multimedia Motion CD-ROM. Available from Cambridge Science Media, 354 Mill Road, Cambridge CB1 3NN.

Newsline Magazine. The Engineering and Physical Sciences Research Council. 'Cars give snapshot of internal combustion', 'Why Computers beat crash test dummies', 'Ultra green scheme for future city transport', 'Cars get smart in the motoring revolution', 'How vehicle technology is moving up a gear' (no. 6, April 1996). Obtainable from EPSRC, Polaris House, North Star Avenue, Swindon SN2 1ET.

Nicholl, B. (ed.) (1980) *Physics at Work*. BP Education Service and the Association for Science Education, London. This details some simple experimental work on electrostatic safety in transportation.

Ramsey, D. C. (1984) *Engineering Instrumentation and Control*, 2nd edn. Stanley Thornes, Cheltenham. A very good introduction to sensors, choosing them, how they work. It even has some model investigations to do.

SATIS 16–19 (1990–2) The Association for Science Education, Hatfield. Many related units worthy of attention: 23 *Stick or Slip*, 47 *Playing Safe*, 48 *Traffic Accident Investigations*, 72 *Cracking Up*.

SATIS 14–16 (1986–91) The Association for Science Education, Hatfield. A couple of units worthy of attention if not used in earlier years: 205 *Looking at Motor Oil*, 504 *How Safe is Your Car*.

Scibor-Rylski, A. J. (1984) *Road Vehicle Aerodynamics*, 2nd edn. Pentech Press, London. An excellent insight into this area.

Setright, L. J. K. (1972) *Automobile Tyres*. Chapman and Hall, London. Somewhat dated, but the definitive text looking at the technology of tyres.

Tao, P. K. (1987) *The Physics of Road Traffic Accident Investigation*. Oxford University Press and Hong Kong Association for Science and Mathematics Education, Hong Kong. This has lots of worked examples relating to physics in road traffic accidents.

Tricker, R. A. R. and Tricker, B. J. K. (1966) *The Science of Movement*. Mills and Boon, London. The classic text on this subject and well worth looking at if you can get hold of a copy.

van der Plas, R. (1983) *The Penguin Bicycle Handbook*. Penguin, Harmondsworth. If you are keen on looking into transportation by bicycle then this is excellent. Lots of useful data and book references too.

Which? Reports. 'How safe is your car?' (October 1989); 'Are your babies sitting safely?' (May 1990); 'Safe in a crash?' (January 1993); 'Sitting safely' (report on which video was based) (August 1993); 'Tyres on test' (April 1994); 'When it comes to the crunch' (February 1995) (report on which video was based); 'How safe is your car?' (February 1995); 'Safer cycling' (April 1995); 'Best buy update – tyres' (August 1995); 'Tyres on test' (April 1996); *Guide to New and Used Cars 1993*, in particular the item 'Safety matters'; *Guide to New and Used Cars 1995*. The Consumers' Association, London.

Acknowledgements

Grateful acknowledgement is made to the following sources for permission to reproduce material in this unit:

Photographs and figures

p. 8: Racing car – A.F.P. Photo, Paris; p. 14: Torque wrench – Mike Levers, The Open University; p. 17: Fork-lift truck on ramp – Boss Group Ltd., Leighton Buzzard; p. 22: Tractor on weighbridge – University of Cranfield Agricultural Engineering Department, Silsoe, Bedfordshire; p. 25: Fork-lift truck – Boss Group Ltd., Leighton Buzzard; p. 31: Airbag – Ford of Britain; p. 37: Child safety seat – Nick Wright; Figure 3.3 – Cambridge Science Media; p. 46: Figure 3.9 – adapted from Macmillan, R. M. (1984) 'Studying vehicle collisions', *Physics Bulletin*, vol. 35, no. 7; p. 47: Figure 3.10 – adapted from Macmillan, R. M. (1984) 'Studying vehicle collisions', *Physics Bulletin*, vol. 35, no. 7; p. 55: Michael Rosswess, sprinter – The Press Association, London; Ford Mondeo – Ford of Britain; p. 66: Isaac Newton – Mansell Collection; p. 97: Leonardo da Vinci – The Mansell Collection; Leonardo da Vinci's apparatus – The Science Museum; p. 98: Electron microscope photograph – Naomi Williams, The Open University; p. 101: Skid marks – Mike Levers, The Open University; p. 107: Anti-lock braking system – Ford of Britain; p. 112: Jennie Constable; Ski slope bristles – British Aerospace Dynamics Group; p. 117: Action on a ski slope – British Aerospace Dynamics Group; p. 129: Streamlined flow – Robin Roy, The Open University; p. 132: Advanced passenger train – British Railways Board; Harrier Jump Jet – Times Newspapers Ltd.; p. 133: James Joule – BBC Houlton Picture Library; p. 137: Air flowing in a wind tunnel – Ford of Britain; p. 141: Figure 9.7 – Heinemann Educational Books/Five Ways Software; p. 143: Figure 9.8 – Heinemann Educational Books/Five Ways Software; p. 144: Figure 9.9 – Heinemann Educational Books/Five Ways Software; p. 146: Tanker refuelling aircraft – Esso Petroleum Company Ltd.

Text

p. 66: Newton's big ideas – Farman, J. (1991) *A Suspiciously Simple History of Science and Invention,* Piccadilly Press, London; p. 97: Leonardo da Vinci – *Comptons Encyclopaedia*.

The authors and Management Group would also like to thank: Boss Group Limited, Leighton Buzzard, Beds; J. Bolton and Son, Lyme Regis, Dorset; Jennie Constable and British Aerospace Dynamics Group, Stevenage, Herts, for permission to adapt material from the article 'Faster longer-lasting skis for artificial ski slopes' in *Aerospace Dynamics*, no. 13, 1984; County Marketing Limited, Dunstable, Beds; Mars Money Systems, Slough, Berks; Jeff Daniels, 'Raising the wind', in *Car Performance*, 1994; University of Cambridge Local Examination Syndicate A-level Modular Board for exam questions; Northumberland County Council; Institute of Physics, 76 Portland Place, London W1N 4AA, for permission to adapt the article 'Studying vehicle collisions'.

Index